YAS

W9-AXI-089

FLORENCE NIGHTINGALE

Florence Nightingale

FLORENCE NIGHTINGALE

By JEANNETTE COVERT NOLAN

Illustrated by

GEORGE AVISON

The Junior Literary Guild and
Julian Messner, Inc.
New York

PUBLISHED BY JULIAN MESSNER, INC.
8 WEST 40TH STREET, NEW YORK 18

PRINTED IN THE UNITED STATES OF AMERICA

CONTENTS

1	Lea Hurst—Summer, 1833	3
2	Holiday Season	15
3	Morning Incident	24
4	Growing Up	34
5	Young Lady of Leisure	44
6	Travels and Dreams	55
7	Glimpse of a Mission	65
8	First Freedom	73
9	The Call to Service	85
10	Journey and Arrival	94
11	A Lady with a Lamp	103
12	Crimean Days	110
13	Problems and Solutions	121
14	Scutari Winter	131
15	"The Daughter of England!"	143
16	Adventure's Ending	154
17	A New Summons	162
18	More Lamps Lighted	172
19	Heroine's Progress	181
20	At Home in South Street	191
21	Trials and Triumphs	200
22	Farewells	207

ILLUSTRATIONS

Florence Nightingale	Frontispiece
"Aren't you enjoying the party?"	7
Cantering along the narrow paths which wound through the clover fields	21
He endured the treatment with patience	31
She recorded it all in her diary	40
"Will you let me be a nurse?"	51
She and Sidney bent over the specifications	59
She wielded the heavy brush	69
The committee bowed to her imperious edict	82
Soldiers were dying of neglect	87
"The English nurse has come"	101
She stepped out upon the upper gallery	103
"Open the warehouse door!"	115
It was mostly hushed	129
"We've come to help you with the nursing"	132
There were large ships anchored in the harbour of Balaclava	143
She had to go on horseback	156
Promptly renamed him the Bison	167
She listened to what they said	173
This was their farewell	184
She might seem little and fragile	194
She witnessed the arrival of the Grenadier Guards	205
She was softer with the years	207

FLORENCE NIGHTINGALE

1

LEA HURST—SUMMER, 1833

FLORENCE LET THE heavy front door swing shut behind her. Then she crossed to the edge of the flagged terrace and paused a moment, frowning slightly. Her arms were filled with dozens of small paper-wrapped packages, each tied with a bit of red or yellow ribbon, and her cheeks were a little flushed from the effort of balancing this burden. She looked anxiously about, to see that nothing had been dropped; she looked again at the packages, her lips moving silently.

Reassured, she smiled and the frown vanished.

No, she had not miscounted; there would be a gift for every person at the party, no one had been forgotten—which meant that all the elaborate plans, her own, Mamma's and Parthe's, had worked out perfectly.

"And a good thing!" thought Florence who, at thirteen, had no patience with plans which failed.

The terrace was cool, shadowed by the stone walls of the house, mellow and vine-hung, rising up to the roof's pointed gables which were like so many conical, dark hats lined against the pastel blue of the sky and the fresh green of the summer trees. From here could be viewed the whole sweep of lawn, orderly, well-tended, luxuriant as bolts of green velvet unrolled in a draper's shop. But beyond the lawn lay the warm, sunlit meadow, overgrown with wild flowers and straggly with low stone fences, where today order abruptly ceased in a gay riot of flashing color and sound.

The party! What a celebration it was, this traditional gathering of the village schoolchildren for the annual entertainment at Lea Hurst, Squire Nightingale's Derbyshire estate. Since early morning the meadow had brimmed with merriment: songs, shouting, laughter so boisterous as to dim the roar of the Derwent River over there among its purple hills; games, dancing, a picnic luncheon spread on the grass under the alders. Now the afternoon waned, but festivities continued, and soon would come the climax of everything, the bountiful tea to be served on tables decorated with bunting and streamers—and finally the distribution of the "treats."

"I suppose," Florence thought, "it must be nearly tea time this instant, and Mamma will be wondering what's become of me." She glanced at the gold watch pinned to the ruffles of her cambric bodice. Four o'clock? She must hurry! Walking briskly, she started toward the hedge which bordered the lawn—and stopped.

On the far side of the thick boxwood someone was running and calling her name. "Florence? *Flo*?"

It was her sister's voice, and Florence waited. "Hello, Parthe!"

"Where are you, Flo?"

"Here, in plain sight." As Parthe darted through a gap in the hedge and appeared, out of breath and curls flying, Florence added calmly, "I was in the house, tying up the packages. Do you want me?"

"Yes." Parthe halted and pressed a hand to her heart. She was fourteen, a year older than Florence, but not so tall; an exceptionally graceful girl with delicate features and a complexion like English strawberries and cream. "Oh, I've *rushed*. Mamma sent me to fetch you."

"Why?" Florence asked. "Anything wrong?"

"Very wrong." Parthe nodded vigorously. "Libby Brown—you know her?"

"Of course, I know her; and her grandmother too—all the Browns."

"That Libby!" Parthe said, grimacing.

"But what's she *doing*, for heaven's sake, to distress you?"

"Oh, not me," Parthe said. "It's Mamma. Libby's doing nothing—that's the trouble. She's just *sitting*. And *moping*. She won't join in the contests or ride on the ponies. Papa volunteered to take her to the kennels to see the dogs—she wouldn't go. She won't talk to any of us or even to the other children. As you may imagine, poor Mamma is terribly upset by such behavior. Mamma can't bear it unless everybody is *happy* at the party. Everybody! So she told me to fetch you immediately. You're to *make* Libby happy—the stupid little creature!"

"Not stupid," Florence said. "Just shy and self-conscious. If you understand Libby—"

"*I* don't," Parthe said, "nor does Mamma. But you have that strange knack of understanding strange people—so you simply must go to the rescue, Flo. Give me the parcels. I'll get a basket for carrying them in, and I promise not to spill them. Hasten now, darling, on your errand of mercy, or whatever it is."

Florence surrendered the beribboned armload; she brushed back the brown hair from her shoulders and straightened her billowing skirts. "Where'll I find our moping Libby?"

"Hiding among the cabbages, probably. At least, I saw

her plodding in the direction of the kitchen garden a while ago. I wish you luck," Parthe said. "And don't pretend you mind, because you know you don't!"

As Florence turned and trudged along the path which led to the kitchen garden, she was both rueful and smiling. Always, it seemed, the difficult guests at Lea Hurst, the lonely or awkward ones, fell to her lot, to comfort and cheer. But Parthe's comment was true. Florence had enacted the role of rescuer so often that she didn't mind it. Perhaps she did, indeed, have a talent for understanding people.

"That might be a valuable thing to have," she thought.

Libby Brown was not among the cabbages. Libby had trailed from the vegetable beds into the apple orchard. When at last Florence spied her, she was crouched forlornly on a bench in the fence corner, a scrawny and unattractive child of eleven, her chin propped on doubled fists, elbows on knees. At Florence's approach, she scrambled up and curtsied.

"No, don't, Libby," Florence said, sitting down quickly. "What's the matter? Aren't you enjoying the party?"

Libby crimsoned with embarrassment, but she was frank. "Well, I'm not, Miss Florence, and that's a fact! Not that anyone's to blame except me. Your mother and father, Miss Parthe and everybody has been kind as kind. They've tried. But it's all too noisy, the boys pushing and the girls yelling as if out of their senses. I like being quiet, I'd rather be at home with Granny." She sighed. "I guess I'm just queer, or something."

"Oh, I don't think you're queer," Florence said soothingly.

"Don't you?"

"No, and I know how you feel. I like being quiet, my-self."

"*Do* you?"

"Aren't you enjoying the party?"

"Yes," Florence said, "and whenever I want to be very quiet, I go upstairs to the old nursery. That's the quietest place in the world; only the dolls live there now. Libby, why don't you go up to the nursery with me? I'll show you the dolls and you can play without any interruptions or bothering; you can have your tea brought up and eat with the dolls."

"Would—would that be all right?" Libby's eyes brightened. She had heard of the collection of dolls in the Nightingale sisters' nursery.

"Oh, certainly," Florence said, getting to her feet. "Come."

Obediently, Libby slid off the bench and followed, her stout, square-toed boots scuffing the gravel, blissful anticipation dawning in her thin face.

The nursery, a spacious room with oak-beamed ceiling and mullioned windows, was on the top floor of the house; two flights of stairs had to be climbed to reach it. But Libby Brown didn't begrudge the exertion. From the moment the door was opened and she entered, Libby was in a state of enchantment, her shyness fading away as she trotted about, inspecting everything and pelting Florence with eager questions.

"How many toys! Are they yours?"

"Yes, mine and Parthe's."

"And books! And the little desks—do you have your lessons here?"

"Not any more." Florence had mounted a stool and was lifting down from a row of shelves the miniature trunks in which the dolls were kept. "We're too big now; we could scarcely fold our long legs under the desks, could we? We don't study much at Lea Hurst. This is our vacation. When we go back to Embley, lessons will begin again."

"Embley? Where's that?"

"In Hampshire. Embley's our other home, where we spend the autumn and winter."

"Every year?"

"Yes, every year."

"And the spring, Miss Florence?"

"Yes, unless we're staying in London then, as we often are."

"Are the lessons hard?"

"Awfully hard," Florence said. "History, mathematics, Latin and Greek. And Papa teaches us Italian. Papa is a *strict* teacher, much stricter than Miss Christie, our governess. He has us write essays, one each week, to improve our grammar and spelling."

"I wouldn't like writing the essays."

"I don't like them, either," Florence confessed. "Parthe's better at them than I am. Parthe's better at all the lessons."

"But why do you have another home?"

"Well, that's because of Papa." Florence jumped down from the stool and searched in a bureau drawer for keys to the trunks. "Papa is a Derbyshire man by birth; his people all lived in this part of England, and he dearly loves it. When he and Mamma were married, they settled at the Hall—Lea Hall, you know, just across the valley, the old farm which Papa inherited from his Great-uncle Peter Nightingale. But the farmhouse was inconvenient, and damp and cold and not very big, so Papa built Lea Hurst, this house. Then later he and Mamma were visiting in Hampshire and they saw Embley Park, and it was for sale, and they thought it was so beautiful that they must buy it—so they did."

"If *I* lived at Lea Hurst," Libby said, "I'd never go to Embley or anywhere else. I wouldn't *budge*."

"Wouldn't you? But Embley is very nice, too, and close to London, when Papa has to travel to the city on business."

"Nicer than Lea Hurst?"

"Maybe not. No," Florence said, "I couldn't choose between them, really. I almost cry when it's time to leave Lea Hurst in September—but, somehow, I'm every bit as sad at leaving Embley in the spring. Oh, Libby, the keys! Here, you may unlock the trunks and unpack them."

For the next quarter-hour, Libby, who liked being quiet, was quiet as a little mouse, exploring the contents of the trunks, carefully taking out and examining the dolls, which were of all sizes and varieties—big waxen lady dolls with wigs of golden hair; bisque babies with painted heads and jointed, muslin bodies; China dolls, French dolls, rag dolls stuffed with sawdust—while Florence stood by, watching.

Then Libby looked up, her expression bewildered.

"Why are so many of them *bandaged?* Are they *sick?*"

Florence smiled. "The bandaged ones are mine. Yes, they were always sick; or at any rate, I used to play they were. I always had them breaking their bones, or coming down with cholera or boils or rashes or something."

"But why?"

"So that I could put on poultices and plasters and give them medicine, and nurse them until they were well. Only I never allowed them to get entirely well—see, they have on their nightgowns—because that would have been so uninteresting."

"Were Miss Parthe's dolls sick, too?"

"Not at first. But they caught the diseases from mine, of course, though Parthe made an awful fuss about it."

"She didn't like to nurse them?"

"No, so I nursed them for her. But Parthe insisted on her dolls recovering *completely*, and wouldn't have it any other way. These are her babies, all dressed in their proper clothes."

"I like Miss Parthe's best," said Libby.

Florence picked up a rag doll and scrutinized it, her gray eyes tender with reminiscence. "This poor dear! She had a dislocated spine which I never could cure. She was my favorite. I practiced on her for ages."

"But, Miss Florence, I don't see *why*."

"Oh, because I wanted to be a nurse. I still want to be one. It's my ambition. I'm *going* to be!"

"A *nurse*?" Libby said. "You can't!"

"That's what Mamma tells me," Florence murmured. "That's what everybody says. But I will."

There was a short silence, and a tapping at the door. A white-capped maid peered into the room.

"Miss Florence, they've finished the tea, and Squire wishes you please to help with the treats."

"Thank you, Clemence. Will you bring Libby Brown a tray up here? Something special, and plenty of the raisin cake. You'll excuse me, Libby? You can manage by yourself."

"Oh, yes," said Libby confidently.

In the meadow, excitement was at fever pitch, with the young guests swarming around a central table which was presided over by Parthe and heaped high with the mysterious packages. Taking up a position opposite her sister, Florence thought that Libby's description had been accurate—the boys were pushing, the girls yelling as if out of their senses. As for Parthe, she looked utterly confused, like an old hen surrounded by a flock of unruly, capering chicks. But Florence saw that Mamma and Papa had remained serene. Seated in two large wicker armchairs behind the table, and somewhat separate from the milling throng, Mamma and Papa looked the very picture of benevolent, adult prosperity and might well have posed as the handsomest couple in the British Isles —as more than once they had been said to be.

With Florence's arrival on the scene, the passing out of the presents commenced; and as each child received his "treat"—it might be a ball or a tin horn, a set of dominoes or a wooden spade and pail—loud exclamations of delight burst forth.

"Oh, awful!" groaned Parthe, holding her ears. "What lungs they have! My word! But Papa's getting up now and it'll soon be over."

Yes, Mr. Nightingale was standing, clapping his hands. He made an announcement, "Children, we'll all sing together. *God Save the King.*"

They hushed, and then sang, " 'God save our gracious King!' "—all the verses of it, bravely and earnestly, with the Squire himself leading in a robust baritone, and the hills echoing the melody.

That was the end of the party, as everybody realized; the signal for farewells. Reluctantly everybody went home.

As the flurry of departures subsided, Parthe collapsed in the grass and leaned against Mamma's knee. "Isn't this a relief? Isn't the peace simply wonderful?"

"Are you tired, dear?" Mamma stroked Parthe's curls.

"I'm exhausted. I love the party, and I love it's being over."

"But it was very successful, wasn't it?" Mamma smiled, fanning herself with a wisp of lace. She turned to Papa. "William, don't you think it was successful?"

"Yes. Yes, indeed." Papa got out his own kerchief, a huge square of white linen and mopped his brow.

"Where's Florence? Ah, there you are, Flo. Come away, daughter, the servants will clear up all that mess on the tables. Well, were you satisfied with the event?"

"I don't know." Florence patted Papa's shoulder affectionately.

"What!" He slipped an arm around her waist. "You don't know?"

"It was all just fine. But—was it enough, Papa?"

"Why, Florence!" Mamma said, glancing up, astonished. "Whatever do you mean? I'm sure the children appreciated it, they had such a good time. I've never seen them so happy." She paused, her pretty face pink, her blue eyes clouding. "But you may be right. Maybe we *don't* do enough. We're so fortunate, we have so much. We must share—"

"Oh, Mamma!" Parthe said. "Flo's always having these odd notions. Pay no attention. Who could do more than you, or be more charitable and generous? The villagers adore you—we all adore you. You're the good woman of the Bible, the one in Proverbs who stretches out her hands to the poor and reaches forth to the needy, and everybody rises to call her blessed."

"Yes," Papa said. " 'Her price is far above rubies. Her husband praiseth her.' But is that what Florence means?"

"No, it isn't, Papa!"

"What *do* you mean?" Parthe said.

Florence hesitated. "I'm afraid I can't quite—well, for the children the party *was* enough—and you *are* just splendid to the villagers, Mamma, and they do love you. But, I mean, is it enough for *us*? Caring for the poor is now only a little part of our lives, something extra. But oughtn't we do it all the time?"

"And do nothing else? Oh, Flo," Parthe cried, "how silly! Why then we should have no time to ourselves."

"I suppose it is rather silly," Florence said. "But—"

"Libby Brown!" Parthe exclaimed suddenly. "Where *is* she?"

"Oh!" Florence said. "I forgot. She's in the nursery."

"She should have gone home with the rest of the children," said Mamma. "Her grandmother will be vexed."

"Never mind, my dear," said Papa. "I'll have one of the grooms drive Libby home in the pony-cart."

2

HOLIDAY SEASON

THE NIGHTINGALES were people of prominence not only in Derbyshire and Hampshire, but also in London; both Mamma and Papa had distinguished connections everywhere. Before her marriage, Mamma had been Frances Smith, daughter of William Smith, who for forty years was a member of Parliament, a man possessing wealth, social position, a large and satisfactory family, and an enviable reputation as the advocate of religious freedom and the protection of the underprivileged.

The William Smith country place was Jermyns, in Essex; there Mamma had spent the happiest possible childhood, growing up to be a charming and popular belle. In 1818 Mrs. William Smith had written to a friend, "Our beautiful Fanny is to marry young Nightingale." Everyone had thought it an excellent match.

At Jermyns, and at her father's London house, Mamma had learned to be a perfect hostess, and now nothing pleased her so much as to entertain visitors; indeed, she was famous for her hospitality. Perhaps Papa was less enthusiastic about the steady flow of "company" through the gates at Lea Hurst and at Embley—his interests were scholarly and agricultural, concerned with his books (especially the philosophical and religious books) and with his acres of land, which were tilled by tenant-farmers—

but he was devoted to his "beautiful Fanny," and very proud of her; he indulged her every fancy.

It was Mamma's wish that the two girls, Parthe and Florence, should have as secure and serene a youth as her own had been; she expected them to like the same pastimes; she hoped that they too would some day be the wives of worthy husbands and manage households similar to hers. In Parthe's case, these ideas of Mamma's seemed certain to bear fruit, for Parthe agreeably accepted them all. But about Florence, Mamma was not so sure.

As Parthe had said, Florence had odd notions. Was she also a little stubborn? Yes, Mamma and Parthe thought that perhaps she was—in a polite and sweet-tempered way, of course; which, as everybody knows, is the most wearisome sort of stubbornness to combat and overcome.

For one thing Florence often grew bored with the confusion which a houseful of even the best-mannered guests can create. Then she would take long, solitary walks through the fields and woods; or seek companionship with her pets, the ponies, the dogs, the ducklings, the tame squirrels scampering on the lawn. Sometimes she would go and sit in the chapel at Lea Hurst, thinking, losing herself in a dream of all the noble deeds she wanted to accomplish when she was older, wiser and more independent.

The chapel was a small structure which had been on this very spot since the days of Queen Elizabeth and it was really a part of the house, for Papa, who liked historical relics, had built Lea Hurst's strong stone walls right around the chapel. On Sundays a village Bible class met in the chapel, but on weekdays it was deserted, an interior swimming with pale yellow reflections of the sunshine outdoors, and so still that you could hear the branches of elms and oaks scratching on the roof.

Whenever Florence went into the chapel, she would think (for a while, at least) about God—because she enjoyed thinking about Him at any time, and it seemed to her particularly easy to believe and trust in Him here. She could even imagine that He was beside her, hovering close, and ready to listen to anything she might say to Him. She knew that, as Mamma and Papa had always told her, God was good; and the knowledge of His unfailing goodness made her yearn to do something (a really large and useful something!) toward the winning of His kingdom on earth. She hoped that God wouldn't object if she preferred to worship like this, alone in the chapel's seclusion, rather than by attending the regular Sunday church services—from which she occasionally absented herself on the plea of a headache. After all, the spirit of worship was what mattered, wasn't it, and not the form?

Having thought about God, Florence's attention would wander to other subjects, perhaps to Papa whom she loved so much. Not that she didn't love Mamma and Parthe also—of course, she did! But probably there was no harm in admitting that she was fondest of Papa, and felt a peculiar bond of sympathy with him.

Florence thought of Papa as an unusual man; and, to begin with, his name was unusual, because he hadn't been born a Nightingale at all. No, his parents were Mr. and Mrs. William Shore, and Papa had been named for his father; as William Shore he was known in his native Derbyshire, at the university in Edinburgh, and again at Trinity College, Cambridge, where he took his graduate degree. But his mother had been a niece of old

Peter Nightingale of Lea Hall, who wanted young William Shore to be the heir to his extensive estates; so, when he was twenty-one and no longer a minor in the eyes of the law, Papa had got his surname legally changed to Nightingale, as a tribute of gratitude and respect to the memory of Great-uncle Peter. After that, Papa was William Shore Nightingale; and now it was almost forgotten that his name had ever been anything else.

In fact, Papa believed that a name should *mean* something, everybody's name, and not be merely a tag, without rhyme or reason, which you must wear forever, whether you liked it or not; with this principle in mind, he had selected the names for his daughters. For the first three years of their married life, he and Mamma had traveled in Europe; they were in Italy, at Naples, when their first child was born, and Papa had said the baby must be called Parthenope, which was the name of the ancient Greek settlement originally on that site. Then, a year later, on May 12, 1820, at the Villa Colombaia, near the Porta Romana in Florence, a second little girl was born to the Nightingales.

"Her name," said Papa, "will be Florence."

Perhaps some people would have regarded this method of naming children as whimsical (and, in Parthe's case, rather *too* whimsical—though certainly Parthenope was better than Naples, which would have been strange, indeed!); but Florence approved of it, as she approved of everything Papa did. He was such a dashing figure of an English country-gentleman—sturdy and tanned, immaculately dressed in high white stock, plush-collared coat and tight-fitting trousers buckled down under the soles of his well-burnished boots. Papa was humorous and mild, never scolding; his daughters had never known him to be angry. Perhaps he was, if anything, too lenient in disposition; or perhaps he only seemed so because in his leisurely existence there were few occurrences to provoke him.

Somehow the school party was always a turning-point in the summer; afterward, the weeks fairly flew by, bringing nearer the time when the Nightingales, bag and baggage, servants and all, would move to Embley. As Florence had remarked to Libby Brown, the process was one to be viewed with mingled emotions. At Embley she would see many old friends, including various families of cats, spaniels and rabbits, and the horses in the stables; and she would be reunited with Miss Christie, the governess, who was a dear person. From Embley there might be a trip or two to Grandfather Smith's house in London. But Florence was sorry to think of Lea Hurst, empty and shuttered through the winter. How lonely it would be until the owners came again!

During the last week of August, Mamma made daily excursions to the village, for she could never have left without knowing that all the tenants were well provided with food, blankets and substantial clothing. It was re-garded as a matter of course that Florence should ac-company her and call on the invalids. According to Parthe's teasing comment, Flo always preferred ill peo-ple to healthy people—to an extent, this was true. In the basket on Florence's arm would be bunches of flowers, jars of broth or jelly, bottles of liniment; she knew just how to shake up a pillow, or brew a cup of tea or stir a pot of porridge. Her manner unhurried and soothing, she was content to sit a while by the sickbed, talking, telling a story, reading a chapter from the Bible.

But she did not like being thanked for such kindnesses; she shrank from compliments or praise. When old Granny Brown hailed her as an "angel child," she was quite wretched.

"Bless you, Miss Florence! Ah, what a grand little lady she is, what a gentle way she has with her!"

"I wish they wouldn't," Florence thought, blushing. "I'm not doing it for *that*."

If only the sick people could have been as silently receptive and unprotesting as were the sick dolls!

On the last day of the week, with all the villagers, ill or healthy, ministered to, Mamma gave Florence and Parthe permission to ride their ponies across the valley to Lea Hall, where Great-uncle Peter Nightingale had lived. They went in the afternoon, cantering along the narrow path which wound through the clover fields, then up the hill to the crest and the old, old gray stone house set in a thicket of giant rose bushes and clustering trees. The Hall had no occupants now; the girls got down from their side-saddles and walked all around and peeped through the bluish, cobwebbed windowpanes.

"From here," Parthe said, "I get glimpses of the staircase. Remember the twisted balustrade, Flo? Remember how we played on the steps when we were little?"

"Let's peep in at the kitchen," Florence said, "and remember Anthony Babington."

"And the conspiracy? Yes, let's!"

On tiptoe, hands shading their eyes, they looked into the kitchen, a room of ample proportions, with heavy-timbered roof and a huge stone hearth, equipped with copper kettles and roasting-spit.

"There's the trap-door to the attic chamber!" Parthe

exclaimed. "Can't you just imagine Babington's comrade, the young nobleman, hiding in the attic, waiting, quaking in his boots—being caught?"

Cantering along the narrow paths which wound through the clover fields

Florence nodded and began to speak, slowly, as though she recited a history assignment: "Almost two hundred and fifty years ago, when Elizabeth was on the throne, this house was known as Dethick. Then it was the home of Henry Babington and his son Anthony—"

"And it was larger, Flo," said Parthe, interrupting.

"Oh, yes. Much larger, very different, with turrets and balconies, galleries and ballrooms and an underground passage—"

"Which led to Wingfield Manor, where Mary Stuart, Queen of Scots, was kept a royal prisoner by Elizabeth!"

"Perhaps," Florence said. "Anyway, many people believed the passage led to Mary's prison. Young Anthony Babington was a stanch supporter of Mary Stuart; he had lived in Paris and there he pledged his fealty to her. When he returned to England he joined the secret organization which was plotting to release her, and often the meetings of the secret society were held here at Dethick."

"Right in this kitchen!" Parthe said. "And when the plot was discovered some of the conspirators fled to this house, and Elizabeth sent her soldiers to seek them here. Well, go on, Flo."

"At night the soldiers came," said Florence, "and burst open the door; and though they didn't find Anthony Babington himself, they did find others of the plotters, and seized them and dragged them off in irons. One man had crept through the ceiling trap into the chamber above, but somehow the soldiers knew it, and they got up on benches and forced up the trap-door, and so they captured him too. Then they went back along the road and presently they did find poor Anthony and arrested him; they took him to London—where he and all the society members were beheaded."

"Then," said Parthe, "Mary was tried and *she* was executed. Oh, what a tragic tale! Would you like to be a queen, Flo?"

"What? And have my head cut off?"

"Elizabeth's head was never cut off."

"But Mary's was. No, I should hate being a queen."

"Such terrible things don't happen nowadays. It mightn't be so bad," Parthe said. "Queens never have to work, you know."

"But I want to work, Pop."

"As a nurse, I suppose?"

"Yes. Why not?"

"Oh, you've been told so often, Flo! Nurses are never ladies. They're just dreadful *women*, slaving in dreary, dirty old hospitals—"

Now it was Florence who interrupted. "Hadn't we better go? Mamma said an early supper."

"Oh, yes," Parthe said, quickly diverted. "Early, because tomorrow we start for Embley. How lovely! You do like Embley, don't you, darling? Even if the village isn't so big? There are always a *few* invalids at Embley."

Florence knew that her sister was mocking her just a little, but she was not annoyed. Smiling, she swung up on the pony's back. Nothing Parthe said could annoy her. Nor could it shake her determination.

"Pop doesn't see," she thought. "She simply doesn't *see*."

3

MORNING INCIDENT

MR. NIGHTINGALE liked to drive in his own carriage all the way from Lea Hurst to Embley, taking his time and stopping frequently en route at the homes of friends or relatives in neighboring counties. Thus, the journey, though long, was never tedious—and the exact date and hour of arrival was of no slightest consequence, because the servants would have gone before, by more direct roads, to open and air the Hampshire house and put the furnishings in exquisite order.

The weather was fine, still warm but with an autumnal moistness and a transparent vapor shimmering above the bogs and heaths, the lakes and woods and flowering copses. When the carriage turned at last between the gateposts of Embley and bowled along the graveled lane and halted at the door, Florence thought that never had the immense Tudor house looked so stately and beautiful, or the gardens so luxuriant. Little wonder that Embley Park was a show-place, known as one of the most picturesque estates in all England! Immediately Florence was glad to be here.

The first thing she and Parthe did, after alighting and changing their traveling dresses for more comfortable clothing, was to run out over the lawn, through the rhododendron borders and hedges of azalea and laurel, to inspect the cypress tree on the front terrace. This was the "nursery tree," so called because it grew close to the house and towered high, its upper branches making a canopy of feathery foliage just outside the nursery windows. The nursery tree was old—Florence could not guess at its age—but even in her memory it had sheltered many generations of birds and squirrels; and under its trailing, tent-like boughs, Florence, at nine, had sat to write her autobiography, writing in French ("La Vie de Florence Rossignol") since, as Miss Christie had insisted, this would give her greater proficiency in the foreign language.

Fortunately, the nursery tree seemed now to be in good condition. "We must get some chestnuts and poke them into the holes in the bark," Parthe said. "For the nuthatches—who have probably missed us."

All that day and the next, the girls renewed acquaintance with old treasures and reminders of happy times in the past. There was, for instance, hanging in the hall the portrait of themselves and Mamma, painted by the artist Chalon, several years earlier. Pausing before it, they marvelled at what small children they once had been—

"But you were the taller even then, Flo," Parthe said. "See, I'm perched like an infant on Mamma's knee, while you're standing up like a real person. You do look intelligent! And so stern!"

"I was scared," Florence said. "Scared half to death, because the artist was a stranger. *You* look *pretty*."

They went into the library and got down their textbooks; and then, by the end of the week, Miss Christie had come and they were back at lessons. Almost before they knew it, a routine had been re-established and, under Mamma's expert management, the family life proceeded on smooth schedule. Every morning the Nightingales had prayers together, followed by breakfast and an interval in which Papa read the newspaper aloud at the table. Afterward, the girls went with Miss Christie to the schoolroom to study until noon, when luncheon was ready; then a short period of more study, this time with Papa, who drilled his daughters in history and Italian and talked interestingly about philosophy, of which he knew so much. In the late afternoon there was outdoor exercise before tea in the parlor at twilight; dinner in the evening, and probably some music in the drawing-room; lastly, more prayers and bedtime. Spare moments were devoted to reading or to fine needlework, such as embroidering. Parthe was learning to paint—or trying to, applying herself with diligence to brushes and canvas, palette and tubes of bright-hued pigments; but this was an inclination which Florence could not share. She would watch her sister, smile, suggest or criticize, then turn away to write letters—or add, in her carefully kept diary, further descriptions of "La Vie de Florence Rossignol."

And always there were to stay over Sunday, or longer (a week, maybe, a month) the inevitable visitors with whom Mamma loved to surround herself—Smith cousins, Shore cousins, relatives named Carter and Nicholson. Of them all, Florence liked best Papa's sister, dear Aunt Mai, who had married Mamma's brother, Samuel Smith. Aunt Mai and Uncle Sam were young, and the fact of their double relationship made them seem especially close and sympathetic; Florence was never anything but at ease with them. Indeed, she sometimes thought that Aunt Mai was the most amiable person in the world and Uncle Sam the most sensible. She could discuss with them the dreams she never mentioned to anyone else.

The village on the Park's outskirts was East Wellow; its vicar was the Reverend Mr. Giffard, a good friend of the Nightingales'—a special friend of Florence's. Making his parish rounds, Mr. Giffard never failed to stop in at Embley where he was heartily welcomed. Before his ordination as a clergyman, Mr. Giffard had studied medicine and whenever he called, Florence would engage him in conversations about the care of the sick and injured; unlike many other adults with whom she had contact, he seemed to think this interest not strange or morbid at all, but only natural.

Mr. Giffard was a fine horseman and enjoyed riding briskly over the Hampshire downs. Often he accepted Mr. Nightingale's offer of a mount from the Embley stables; then he would ask Florence to ride with him, and off they would gallop in the autumn sunshine.

One morning an incident occurred which was to linger long in Florence's mind—and in the tradition of East Wellow. Dashing over the billowing green downs, swerving at a hedgerow, the two friends drew rein and rested a minute to look at the pasture beneath them. Florence was breathless, laughing, her hair disarrayed, her hat fallen back on her shoulders. She said that she loved this view—

"Those are old Roger's sheep, Mr. Giffard. They behave so nicely, marching like soldiers, with Cap to guide them."

Mr. Giffard agreed. Yes, he himself had noticed the beautiful manners of Roger's sheep, the white pattern they made against the green pasture. "Roger is a lucky farmer to have such sheep—and a collie as smart as Cap to keep them in line as they graze. There are never any stragglers in the flock Cap tends."

But then Mr. Giffard paused, and gestured. "Miss Florence, something is wrong today!"

She stared at his pointing finger and was dismayed. Something was wrong, indeed! Today the pattern had not its customary neatness; the sheep were shifting, spreading out over the slopes, blundering about, bleating, straying. Cap, the clever collie, was not to be seen.

As they watched, Roger loomed into sight, in the middle of the flock. Roger was waving his arms like a windmill. "Hey!" he shouted. "Stop now—hey!"

"Come," said Mr. Giffard, and he spurred forward with Florence at his side. When he was within speaking range, he called out, "What's the matter, Roger? In trouble, aren't you?"

Roger glanced up, shaking his grizzled head. "That I am, sir. In desperate trouble. Can't get these animals to mind me at all. Plunge here and there they will, and never even look my way!"

"Where's Cap?"

"Ah, poor Cap!" Roger sighed. "Done for, I'm thinking."

"Done for?"

"Yes, sir. The devilish boys on yon farm stoned Cap; broke his leg, they did. He's a sadly hurt dog, poor Cap. I'll have to put him out of his misery."

"Oh, Roger!" Florence cried. "You're not going to kill Cap! You *wouldn't*!"

"Well, I'm afraid I must, missy." Roger tugged respectfully at his forelock, for this was the squire's daughter. "Yes, a bit of rope round his neck, one quick twist—but I'll never have another dog like him, because there never was his like!"

Florence turned from Roger to Mr. Giffard; tears were in her eyes: "Couldn't—couldn't we do something?"

Mr. Giffard looked thoughtful. "Is Cap in your shed now, Roger?"

"No, sir. In my house. Roped up, for he'll not let anyone near him. Snarls and snaps and shows his teeth. Ah, he's in pain, poor Cap! And these pesky sheep! See them go right out of bounds again! If you'll excuse me, sir and missy—" Shouting, Roger started once more in pursuit of the flock.

"Mr. Giffard?" Florence said. "You know so much about medicine. Couldn't we—"

He smiled and slapped his reins. "Perhaps. Come, Miss Florence."

They rode to Roger's house. The door was closed, locked; and from within sounded a violent barking which told of Cap's lonely suffering, his terror that someone would intrude to hurt him even more.

"I think Roger's neighbor will have a key we can borrow," said Mr. Giffard. "I'll get it."

Yes, the neighbor had a key which would fit. In a little while they had opened the door and were entering.

Cap lay stretched on the floor, trembling, rumbling out a hoarse protest of growls. But when Florence spoke to him—"Don't be frightened, Cap. We want to help you,"—he lifted his muzzle and feebly wagged his tail.

Mr. Giffard bent over the dog and very cautiously felt the leg which was badly swollen.

"Is it really broken?" Florence said.

"I'm not quite sure yet. Stand back, Miss Florence. He might bite."

"Oh, no!" Florence went down on her knees, stroking Cap's nose. "Why, we've been friends for years."

Mr. Giffard made his examination, and straightened. "The bone's not damaged. It's a dislocation and some torn ligaments. Serious, but not fatal; the poor chap ought not be destroyed. Hot compresses are the thing—"

"The kettle's on the stove! I'll boil the water!"

"But we have no cloth for the compresses."

"But we have!" Florence jumped to her feet. Old Roger's smock was suspended on a peg in the wall; she snatched it down, ripped it into squares, folded the squares into pads. "Mamma will give Roger another smock. Is this about the right size, Mr. Giffard?"

"Quite right. Now to heat the water! It may be rather a long-drawn-out process, Miss Florence."

"An hour?"

"Or longer. Will your mother be worried?"

"We won't think of that. Not yet," Florence said, smiling. "I can explain to Mamma."

So for more than an hour they applied the hot compresses to Cap's leg and he endured the treatment with patience, as if he understood that they intended only to help him. As the pain diminished, his tail thumped on the floor and he licked Florence's fingers, gazing at her with beautiful brown eyes.

Finally Mr. Giffard said they had done everything possible. "But there should be another treatment tomorrow."

"I'll come tomorrow," Florence said, "and every day until Cap is cured."

At noon they rode slowly homeward. Florence felt elated, jogging beside Mr. Giffard and chattering away more freely than ever before. This, she said, was what she liked—being useful. It was serving God, wasn't it, to work for the good of His creatures, whether these creatures were people or just dumb beasts?

"When I was a very small girl, Mr. Giffard—just six, I decided I was going to be a nurse, because that seems to me the best thing of all to be. I want to work in a hospi-

He endured the treatment with patience

tal, with only ill people around me; I want to make them well. Parthe laughs at me for that; she says nurses are dreadful women. But do they *have* to be dreadful? I don't think so! *I* wouldn't be!"

Mr. Giffard smiled at her eager young face. "My dear Miss Florence, you couldn't be dreadful. I can't picture you as anything except wholly charming. But—hospital work?" He paused. "You have no conception of what it is. How could you have, a little lady of your birth and breeding? I fear Miss Parthe's idea is very near the truth. Conditions in the hospitals are really disgraceful and the characters of the women who work there are not much better."

"Maybe," said Florence, "I could build my own hospital. Papa would build one for me. It need not be a large one. It would be *nice!*"

"Oh, I'm sure you would make your hospital nice. But nursing is scarcely the enterprise for a girl of your station, Miss Florence."

"Not even when I'm older?"

"I'm afraid not. You see, you are a gentleman's daughter."

"What difference does that make?"

"A great deal, perhaps." Mr. Giffard paused again. "It's all difficult to put into words; but in a society such as ours, there are conventions, rules. You say you want to serve God? How admirable! But you could do that in any one of a number of ways."

"What are they, Mr. Giffard?"

"Suppose you married an honest man whom you loved and then reared a family of fine, honorable children. You would then be serving God—"

"I don't think I will," she said. "I'll probably never get married at all."

Mr. Giffard laughed. "You may amend that notion later."

Florence made no response. She did not care to hear

what more the clergyman might have to say. She liked him, but he was mistaken about what she would do. Whoever opposed her was mistaken.

She rode silently, her eyes on the far horizon.

4

GROWING UP

THE YEARS HAD a way of passing, each one pleasantly like the one before. Lessons went on and were constantly more intensive, for Mr. Nightingale's aim was to educate his daughters thoroughly, so that as young ladies they could take their proper place in the cultured circle to which they had been born. But Mamma's training was no less rigorous; her girls must be prepared to marry well, rear families and preside over such houses as they had always known. They must be mindful of their obligations; must never forget the world's vast number of poverty-stricken folk. Charity, Mamma counselled, is the most becoming of all virtues.

The girls listened, believed and followed Mamma's example. But ever in Florence's thoughts flamed the conviction that charity, though beautiful, was not enough. Remembering the unfortunate, working for their betterment, should be one's *sole* occupation. She wished very much that she could see for herself the inside of some of these hospitals which people spoke of as appalling and intolerable. Why were not the hospitals reformed and made perfect? Could not their evils be corrected?

At Lea Hurst, in the brief summer months spent there, Florence took charge of the Bible class which met on Sundays in the quaint little chapel. She had for pupils girls no older than herself—yet very different in experience; they were servant girls, or youthful employees in mills from the towns roundabout who came to the country for a summer outing, some of them coming even as far as from Nottingham, where the big stocking mills flourished. Mr. Nightingale had thrown open his Derbyshire estate to the mill people; there they could camp out, tramp about at will, have a taste of fresh air and sunshine. When the church bells rang on Sunday morning, they could crowd into the chapel and hear Florence read God's word.

Slender and very grave, she would stand before her audience, her dark hair brushed in wings to frame her oval face, a knot at the nape of her neck—perhaps with a rose thrust into it, and another rose pinned to the wide lace collar of her fine silk frock. She would have removed her Leghorn bonnet of "coal-scuttle" size and style, and she wore no other ornaments than the flowers, for she wanted to be as much as possible like these girls in the class; she must talk to them intimately, as if she were one of them.

Yet she was conscious of the fact that she really was not one of them, an invisible chasm yawned between herself and them. They knew so much which she could not know, all the hard things of life, the rough corners and grim realities. Well, she would learn from them! She encouraged them to talk frankly of their labors, their problems. She was the audience then, drinking it all in, thinking. Perhaps she was secretly envious that none of these realities ever approached her except by hearsay.

Once Florence had the privilege of seeing Mrs. Elizabeth Fry, that valiant Englishwoman who was performing such miracles in the reforming of prisons and asylums for the insane. Mrs. Fry's career was well known; in the beginning she had been only a sort of Lady Bountiful to the poor and neglected in her immediate neighborhood. But, investigating farther, she had looked into Newgate prison; the female inmates there were miserably treated, utterly wretched, and she had resolved that something must be done for them and that she was the person to do it. Elizabeth Fry had the vision of a saint, the energy of a zealot. Accomplishing the reformation of Newgate, she carried the fight to similar institutions everywhere.

For Elizabeth Fry and her triumphs young Florence Nightingale had a feeling of awe and reverence. The astonishing thing was that Mrs. Fry's background was so very like Florence's. Elizabeth Fry's family was wealthy, her childhood had been sheltered. Yet, somehow, she had emerged from this background as a strong champion of actual, tangible good.

How had she done that, Florence wondered. What were the steps by which she had forged forward to her goal?

A rare and indomitable person, Elizabeth Fry! You thought of her—and contrasted the battles she had waged and won with your own lot in life, with all its easy circumstances. The weeks all flowing on so smoothly into years, each of which contributed to your benefit and enjoyment; Parthe's high spirits, Papa's solicitude, Mamma's tenderness; the well-managed house-parties at Lea Hurst, the picnics in the grove, the fetes on the lawn; luncheons and dinners at Embley; Christmas Eve and the villagers singing carols under the windows and then being asked in for a jolly supper of gingerbread, hot mince pies and eggnog at a table garnished with holly and mistletoe and silver coins, which were tokens for the singers. All this seemed designed to make you contented with things as they were, to distract you from doubts as to the rightness of the world. Why not just be swept along, unquestioning?

But Elizabeth Fry had rebelled. Some instinct had forced her to probe beneath the surface of her contentment, and what she saw there she must remember always.

Florence Nightingale would probe, too.

When Florence was seventeen, Queen Victoria acceded to the throne of England.

A dramatic event that was; the whole civilized world hummed with the news; at Embley Papa read all about it aloud to the group around the breakfast table. A girl donning the crown of the mightiest kingdom in the universe? And what a very young and unsophisticated girl! "Why, she is only eighteen; your age, Parthenope; only a year older than our Florence." And how plainly and modestly she had been brought up, in gloomy Kensington Palace, where she'd lived almost as a recluse, with just her mother, the Duchess of Kent, and her governess, the German Fräulein Lehzen, as companions.

Wasn't it true that Victoria had never slept a night away from her mother's room? Or been allowed to converse with any adult (friend, tutor or servant) except in her mother's presence? She hadn't known at all, or even suspected, that she was destined to be a queen. Not until she was twelve, when by means of a carefully arranged history lesson, her mother had told her what the future held in store.

Then Victoria had said solemnly, her first words, "I will be good."

The King is dead. Long live the Queen!

In the early hours of June 20, 1837, King William IV, Victoria's uncle, died. The Archbishop of Canterbury and the Lord Chamberlain were bearers of the tidings, posting to Kensington Palace in the shivery gray light of dawn, knocking portentously on the door, being admitted. Long live the Queen! She came walking down the great staircase, roused suddenly from her bed, clad in her padded dressing-gown and slippers. It was five o'clock, the world still and waiting, birds rustling in their nests, the east faintly streaked with pink.

She walked down the stairs, and the august messengers bowed low before her. "Your Majesty!" She was surprised, but very gracious, very dignified.

"I will be good."

A few hours more and the privy council had convened at Kensington, the usual oaths were administered to the Queen by the Lord Chancellor; all witnesses to these ceremonies were moved by the spectacle of Victoria's poise and self-possession. Here was a ruler deserving love and veneration! In the long chronicle of English monarchy, a new and better epoch had begun.

At Embley, as Papa read aloud, Florence thought about the Queen, who wanted most of all to be good, had pledged herself to goodness. The firm statement of intention was not difficult for Florence to understand; she knew what it was like to hear a call to duty and to respond with a vow. There had been that February day in this very year—February 7, 1839, it was; she would never forget it—when abruptly from somewhere a voice had spoken, telling her that she too was to be an instrument of destiny, divinely appointed. The voice was mysterious, not human; it may have been only the stirring of the wind; yet it spoke a clear summons. For so many years

she had wished, with a child's indefinite, diffused longing, to serve God; she had talked of it to anyone who
would not smile—and these listeners, even the politest of
them, had never really known what she meant, their
lack of comprehension had grieved her and encompassed
her in a kind of groping loneliness—but now she was certain of God's call, because on February 7 she had heard
it unmistakably and answered without hesitation.

Yes, she would serve God, and in the way of His selection—which, as it happened, was the way she herself
preferred. The problem of Florence Nightingale's future
was settled!

She recorded it all in her diary; the date, the soft yet
commanding voice calling, calling. Like the young
Queen, Florence had a mission.

"I could not pray for George IV," she was to write,
later. "I thought people very good who prayed for him,
and wondered whether he could have been much worse
if he had not been prayed for. William IV I prayed for a
little. But when Victoria came to the throne, I prayed for
her in a rapture of feeling and my thoughts never wan-
dered."

The Nightingales went abroad that autumn for it was
time, Papa said, the girls had some foreign travel. They
went to France and northern Italy, where they remained
several months and were entertained by their numerous
friends there. They were several more months in Switzer-
land, with a long stay in Geneva. It was Mr. Nightingale's idea that traveling had an educational value and
was not to be undertaken merely for pleasure. His girls
must concern themselves not only with the beauty of the
scenery but also with the art, architecture, literature,
people and laws of these European countries. They must

keep industriously at their studies and make notes in their journals of everything they saw and did.

Perhaps Mr. Nightingale was unaware of the attention which Florence gave to the benevolent institutions

She recorded it all in her diary

in such cities as they visited or her burning curiosity to know more and more about hospitals, prisons and work-houses. Her eyes and ears were constantly open; she observed that here on the continent, as in England, the best and almost the only help extended to the poor, the insane, the diseased or indigent was through the Church and its religious orders, or through the exercise of private charity. The general public had not been roused to any enthusiasm for humanitarian efforts; those few public asylums which existed were places of filth, cruelty and squalor. In every nation the populace seemed to be divided into classes, with lines like fences drawn between. There were the aristocracy, the middle class, the great masses of the poor and oppressed—and only the exceptional person thought much about breaking through the fences and proclaiming the equality of all men's rights.

Genteel people, many of them, referred to the common folk as the "mob" or the "rabble," and assumed that their homes must be hovels, their habits repulsive. Those genteel people endowed with a conscience were not unwilling to assist the common folk to a better mode of life —certainly not! But they did so patronizingly, by way of charity, with the impulsive gesture of a lord flinging his full purse ino the outthrust hand of a beggar.

All this was to be seen in the slums of the world's big cities. Florence Nightingale saw it, and knew, at seventeen, that there were shameful flaws in the universal scheme of things. The flaws must be repaired! But how? The job was of huge proportions—and what could the single worker, toiling alone, hope for?

She would watch, inquire, find out.

It was the autumn of 1838 when the Nightingales left Geneva, going on to Paris to spend the winter. In the French capital they met Mary Clarke, a brilliantly intellectual Englishwoman whose home was a rendezvous for the most distinguished Parisian literary celebrities, and also for men of political fame. Invitations to Miss Clarke's *salon* were sought after; in her drawing-room gathered the elite, conversation scintillated and sparkled like diamonds. She had been instantly on terms of cordiality with all the Nightingales, a friendship which was to last through the years.

Because of Miss Clarke's courtesy in introducing them everywhere, the winter was an exciting one for Florence and Parthe, gay beyond any they had ever known before. Parthe especially threw herself heart and soul into the social program. But Florence too was blithely buoyant, feeling (as she said, somewhat apologetically) the "temptation to shine in society." The young gentlemen who took her in to dinner often had occasion to comment on the sharpness of her wit, her outbursts of humor and her keen appreciation of the ridiculous. She was never so pretty as Parthe; but her eyes were fine, under arched black brows; her features were delicate and sensitive; and her slim height set off to advantage all her new Paris-made costumes.

When in the spring of 1839 the Nightingales returned to England, they had been away eighteen months; and now they would not go directly to Embley or Lea Hurst. They must stop in London, Mamma said, for the "season." The girls must have piano and singing lessons with metropolitan masters, must attend a series of concerts and lectures, and see whatever dramas the London stage was offering. And they must be presented at court. Parthenope and Florence were now quite old enough, their mother thought, for a formal debut; they should have it at once—

As usual, Mamma's plans carried through. "Successfully!" she said. After this, every year they would spend the season in London—until (she probably added, to herself) the girls were properly married. Anyway, she had launched them.

They reached Embley in the early summer. Oh, how lovely it was, the grass and copses green, the shrubbery flowering, roses bending on slender stems in the garden, the nursery tree a haven for the nuthatches, the rhododendrons in lavish bloom.

"I shall always remember the rhododendrons as they look now," Florence thought. "I shall remember them even when I'm quite an old lady!"

Home, so dear, so beautiful—and so unchanged. That really was the astonishing thing, wasn't it? The unchangeableness of Embley and the life to be led there. You left it, were absent for ages; you came back, much more grown-up, your viewpoint broadened, and everything was the same! Somehow you were unprepared for that.

Precisely the same? Well, no. A few alterations had been made in the house itself, some interior decorating done, new bedrooms built. Now, as Florence recorded in a letter, Mamma could have here as guests "five ablebodied females with their husbands and belongings." But these differences were scarcely to be noticed, once the normal tempo of daily life had been resumed.

Embley was the same; when you drove to Derbyshire later, Lea Hurst would be the same, too. Even *tiresomely* the same. In both places luxury closed around you like a downy, warm blanket.

A beautiful blanket, yes. But rather excessively soft. Rather suffocating—wasn't it?

5

YOUNG LADY OF LEISURE

FLORENCE WAS TWENTY-ONE, then twenty-two. And what was she doing with herself?

Well, all the conventional and accustomed things. No more governesses, of course, and no more lessons. Papa was satisfied with his daughters' education, which was far above average. Indeed, they were extraordinarily cultivated young ladies, adept linguists, speaking several languages, including the Italian he'd taught them. In history, mathematics and philosophy they had a solid foundation; they knew a great deal about politics. They were sufficiently musical, anyway as much as fashion required them to be; and Parthe, at least, was interested in art. In their father's eyes they were superbly finished products. Henceforth they should study only as they chose.

Perhaps Papa would have been surprised, had he foreseen the trend which Florence's further studies were to take.

They had a few light tasks to be attended to daily—nothing arduous; rather, something like arranging the flowers or helping Mrs. Nightingale with her charity calls or embroidering an altar cloth for church, or mending their gloves. Then the girls were free to amuse themselves, to dance, sing, stroll with other young people of their own sort, to give fancy-dress balls, charades or tableaux. Once at Waverley Hall, the home of their Nicholson cousins, the Nightingale sisters took part in an amateur performance of *The Merchant of Venice*, directed by William Charles Macready, the eminent Shakespearean actor. Florence was Mr. Macready's stage manager on this occasion—most efficient, so everybody said.

But what of Florence's ambition?

It was not much advanced by the passing years. She continued to look after her villagers—a difficult thing because of the fact that as soon as she was constructively busy in Lea, the calendar dictated moving on again to Embley, or the other way round. After all, she knew this wasn't what a little girl had dreamed of those sunny afternoons in the old chapel, not what had been meant by a small, disembodied voice murmuring in her ear. This was but playing at something which should be done seriously. It was imitation, not reality; and the oppressing thought could never be quite shaken off.

La Vie de Florence Rossignol? She was still writing it, in her diary, in letters to many correspondents. But what was at first a vague distaste became a positive displeasure. The life of Florence Nightingale? The captivity, you might say! She loved her family—oh, yes! She loved her home. But the Lea Hurst hedgerows, the Embley rhododendron borders (if seen at a certain angle) curiously resembled fences with spiked tops, fences she couldn't get over or past. They gave her the feeling of being penned in, shut up within the narrow confines of a plush-lined jewel case. She must get out. She must!

Sometimes, in London for a week or month, her mood was more cheerful. London was an escape of sorts. In the country, she said, there was nothing beyond the necessity of "looking merry and saying something lively, mornings, noons and nights." In the city, "you can at least have the mornings to yourself."

You were spared, for instance, the ordeal of Papa's reading aloud at the breakfast table—

"To be read aloud to," Florence asserted, "is the most miserable exercise of the human intellect. Or rather, is it any exercise at all? It is like lying on one's back with one's hands tied, and having liquid poured down one's throat."

Not so bad for Parthe, perhaps. No, dear Pop could take refuge behind her sketching board while Papa ploughed methodically through the *Times* from the first page to the last. But Florence must sit, listening (or pretending to listen) and be bored.

The others didn't even guess what went on in her mind. That was the worst of it! Well, perhaps Papa understood, just a little, and was sorry. But Mrs. Nightingale and Parthe? Never! Was Florence pouting again, long-faced and silent? Why on earth couldn't she be happy? Hadn't she everything in creation to make her happy?

"It's a mystery!" Parthe declared.

"It's a disappointment," mourned Mamma, "to *me*."

Sometimes Florence solicited advice on how to conquer her dejection. Mary Clarke had a suggestion. Why shouldn't Florence write? A respectable calling for a lady, and Florence had literary ability, as shown in her letters.

"Write something," said Miss Clarke.

But Florence knew her own limitations; she wasn't cut out to be an author. "I think what is not of the first class had better not exist at all," she replied, "and besides I had so much rather live than write; writing is only a substitute for living. I think one's feelings waste themselves in words; they ought all to be distilled into actions which bring results."

She knew what life should be. Exactly. "Life is no holiday game, nor is it a clever book, nor is it a school of instruction, nor a valley of tears; but it is a hard fight, a struggle, a wrestling with the principle of evil, hand to hand, foot to foot." On the margin of a page of poetry, she scribbled her belief: "To find out what we can do, one's individual place, as well as the general end, is man's task."

If she had been a *man*, all would have been so easy for her! Then wealth and social position might have counted not as handicaps but as assets. Rich men's sons could be useful—in politics, for example. But to girls, to young ladies of Florence's kind, all such outlets for energy were forbidden.

Young ladies married; or, unmarried, remained at home. They were sweet, demure—and idle.

A summer visitor to Embley Park was Dr. Samuel Gridley Howe, the American, whose wife, the beautiful and talented Julia Ward Howe was to become a legendary figure in the United States as the author of the *Battle Hymn of the Republic*. Dr. Howe was an internationally famous philanthropist, working to alleviate the lot of blind people everywhere. One morning, as he walked in the rose garden, Florence went timidly up to him.

"Dr. Howe?"

He turned, smiling. "Yes, Miss Florence?"

"Will you answer a question for me? Frankly?"

"I shall be delighted!"

"If," Florence said, her voice very low and vibrant

with emotion, "if I should decide—*really* decide—to study nursing and devote all the rest of my life to nursing—do you think it would be a dreadful thing?"

"No, not dreadful." Dr. Howe stood, looking at the roses, his face grave now, as if he saw the depths of yearning behind the question. "Not dreadful at all. But —unusual, shall we say? In England whatever is unusual is likely to be deemed unfitting."

"Yes, I know. Everyone has told me."

"What everyone says has no effect upon you?"

"No. Because I want so much to be a nurse, I'm sure it is my true vocation! The wish, the hope, is all I care for in the world—" She paused, her grey eyes misty.

"Then," Dr. Howe said, "you must go on with it, without fear. Pursue and accomplish your aspirations. God will be with you."

Florence drew a tremulous breath. Here was advice she could accept! In the presence of this great humanitarian, she felt at ease, could speak unguardedly. She said that she had noted the achievements of the orders of nursing nuns in the Roman Catholic sisterhoods; for such women she had a profound admiration, since with them their profession was an entire religion and even life itself. But why was there not a Protestant organization of this type?

"My dear Miss Florence, there is Pastor Theodor Fliedner's establishment of deaconesses at Kaiserswerth in Germany. Have you not heard of it?"

She hadn't. Kaiserswerth? Stimulated by the mere thought that she was to have a new avenue to explore, she thanked Dr. Howe. He had helped her more than he would ever know.

That summer and the next, Florence gathered information about Kaiserswerth from all available sources, and frequently from the guests at Embley and Lea Hurst, many of whom were celebrities in one or another field of humanitarian endeavor—Sir Joshua Jebb, Surveyor of Prisons; Dr. Richard Dawes, dean of Hereford and educational reformer; Dr. Richard Fowler, experimenting at Salisbury with the open-air treatment of consumption; Mrs. Elizabeth Gaskell, recently coming into prominence with her published sketches of the Manchester slums. Now Mary Clarke was spending a month or two each year with the Nightingales; Florence consulted with her, and with Aunt Mai Smith, who was so faithfully interested.

The theory of nursing was uppermost in Florence's thoughts, something to ponder endlessly. Soon she had the chance for a brief practical experience. At Tapton Grandmamma Shore fell ill, and Florence was sent for. Grandmamma Shore was old and strong-willed; nobody else in the family could make her take her medicine. But she was fond of Florence. Maybe with Florence to care for her, she wouldn't be so unruly a patient.

Florence enjoyed the stay at Tapton in Grandmamma's house. To her cousin, Hilary Bonham Carter, she wrote that she hadn't been so nearly happy for a long time. "I am very glad to walk sometimes in the valley of the shadow of death as I do here." She was glad, too, when Grandmamma recovered.

It must have been at Tapton that she hit upon the wonderful idea of going to study nursing at the Salisbury hospital in Wiltshire. In secret she thought about it —how, having completed the course, she might get a small building in West Wellow, not far from home, and there found a nursing center, staffed by an English sisterhood of nurses which she would head. A fascinating scheme! If only she could get Mamma's consent—

She couldn't. Mamma was shocked. Florence at Salisbury hospital? Waiting upon strangers, dressing their wounds, bending over their beds, nursing them? Florence exposed to association with the regular nurses, uncouth men and ill-bred women who drank to excess (or so people said), used foul language and were obviously riffraff?

"No!" Mamma cried. "Oh, no!"

"Mamma is behaving," said Florence to Parthe, "as if her darling Flo had expressed the desire to be a scullery maid."

"Mamma is right," said Parthe. "Your idea is ridiculous."

Grudgingly then Florence gave it up. To Hilary Bonham Carter she wrote abjectly of her failure: "I shall never do anything, and am worse than dust and nothing. Oh, for some strong thing to sweep this loathsome life into the past!" Yet hope would not quite die. "The longer I live," she wrote in her diary, "the more I feel as if all my being was gradually drawing to one point."

Now Florence thought of asking Papa to get in touch with certain persons in London who could tell him the plain, unvarnished facts about hospitals.

"I am not averse to that," Papa said.

"If what you're told is not too bad, will you let me be a nurse?"

"If," Papa said cautiously, "I think a young lady of your rearing could adapt herself to such an atmosphere, I shall—well, countenance the possibility."

But the descriptions received were anything but reassuring. The stories of hospital life had not, it seemed, been exaggerated. There were vicious and degraded people admitted as patients. As for the nurses, both male and female, they were most reprehensible; scarcely any

"Will you let me be a nurse?"

among them had either good character or ability; they drank, they indulged in improprieties if not in downright immorality.

"Florence," Papa said, "no one stricken with illness ever goes voluntarily into a hospital—where, probably, the nurses can't even be trusted to give a dose of pills without making a mistake!"

"But the hospitals are always full of people."

"People who cannot afford to be sick at home. A deplorable thing, Florence!"

Yes, deplorable—and obviously not for William Shore Nightingale's daughter.

She was twenty-six now, and reading everything about Pastor Fliedner which came her way, snatching at any accounts she could lay hands upon. No tale had ever intrigued her so much.

Pieced together, bit by bit, it went back to 1833, when a Lutheran clergyman in the small German town on the Rhine had furnished the tiny summerhouse behind his own humble dwelling as a shelter for ailing and outcast women. Theodor Fliedner was a widely traveled man (indeed, he had tramped all over Europe and through England as an evangelistic preacher); in London he had talked with Elizabeth Fry. This must have been a meeting of kindred souls, for Fliedner's greatest pity was for the inmates of penal institutions, and especially for women who had suffered imprisonment and then been released as ex-convicts into communities which scorned and persecuted them. These were the poor creatures he most wished to help. Returning to Kaiserswerth, he patched the leaky roof of his summerhouse, made the interior clean and habitable; put in a cot, a chair, a table, let it be known that the place was ready for occupancy— and then prayed that God would send there some friendless wayfarer.

One cold night the first of his charges arrived, stumbling through the darkness, knocking. Herr Fliedner was asleep; his wife wakened him. In his coarse stockings, without boots, he opened the door.

"Welcome, my daughter."

During that winter, nine women came to the pastorage. It was evident that the flimsy sanctuary would have to be enlarged. Where, asked Fliedner's wife, would they get the money?

"The money? It will be provided *Liebchen*."

Somehow, in paltry sums from here and there, the money was provided. Nurses were secured for the ill women, nurses whom Theodor Fliedner himself painstakingly trained. Within three years, he had started a hospital in the wing of a deserted factory, equipping it with discarded odds and ends which he begged from the more prosperous folk of Kaiserswerth. Had he only six sheets for the hospital beds? Ah, but plenty of water to wash them in, and soap was so cheap! His nurses, the deaconesses, served not for wages but in fulfillment of a religious vow—though they could always leave, if they wished, and go back to ordinary life. Another year or two and he had a training school for teachers, an orphanage also; and now in twenty-five European cities his graduate nurses were beginning other hospitals, modeled after Kaiserswerth.

To Florence, Herr Fliedner's story was the one ray of light piercing the bleakness of her own frustration.

July 7, 1846, she wrote in her diary: "What is my business in the world and what have I done this last fortnight? I have read the *Daughter at Home* to Papa, and two chapters of Mackintosh; a volume of *Sybil* to Mamma. Learnt seven tunes by heart. Written various letters. Ridden with Papa. Paid eight visits. Done company. And that is all."

At Embley, October 7: "What have I done the last three months? They don't know how weary this way of life is to me—this *table d'hote* of people."

But she had been perusing the annual report from Kaiserswerth. "There is my home. There are my brothers and sisters all at work. There my heart is and there I trust will one day be my body, whether in this state or in the next, I do not care."

6

TRAVELS AND DREAMS

FLORENCE WAS TWENTY-SEVEN and going to Rome with her good friends, Charles and Selina Bracebridge. The Nightingale sisters offered differing reasons as to why Mamma allowed Flo to set out with just these two companions—a married couple, of course, yet no older than herself. Florence wrote to Hilary Bonham Carter that she hadn't been well: "All that I want to do in life depends on my health, which I am told a winter in Rome will establish forever." But Parthe, also writing to Hilary, confided that Flo had been indulging in "wearing thoughts," she was so pale, her sleep disturbed; duty had weighed too heavily on her conscience and she needed to rest her mind.

Parthe was a little worried about the boldness of Flo's venture—leaving home without her parents! It was a thing which Parthe herself would never have dared—or, for that matter, have enjoyed. When the solemn moment for farewells came, Parthe declared, "My heart is very full of many feelings." Still, she really didn't think that Flo would be harmed by the excursion.

"You must 'do' Rome thoroughly, Flo," Parthe said. "See everything that Papa and Mama saw on their wedding tour. And let us hear from you *often*."

Florence promised. No one must ever know how eager she was to get away!

For such travelers, Rome had many social diversions to extend; but Florence, with her studious temperament, would only sample these and devote most of her vacation to viewing the Holy City's art treasures. The great age, the hugeness and grandeur of Rome, its quality of being eternal and never-changing stirred her to the depths. In her letters home, as frequent and lengthy as Parthe could have wished, she told of how awed she was at beholding gigantic ruins, vast St. Peter's, the glorious sunsets over the wide Campagna, the incredible beauty of Michelangelo's paintings in the Sistine chapel.

Naturally enough perhaps, her thoughts turned to religion; she made a serious study of the Roman Catholic Church, its doctrine and ritual, even going so far as to enter the ten-day Retreat in the Convent of the Trinità dei Monti, where she became fast friends with the Superior, and acquainted herself with the organization and rules of the large school attached to the Convent. Observers wondered whether this reverent and intelligent Englishwoman might not be contemplating joining the Catholic faith—but, if so, her conversion never quite materialized. No, she would remain a Protestant, a member of the Church of England, but she would be always completely tolerant, respecting all sects, seeing the spiritual value in them all, hating bigotry and fanaticism.

In any denomination God could be served. And that alone was worth the doing.

In Rome the Bracebridges encountered some English friends, Sidney and Elizabeth Herbert, to whom Florence was introduced. No one, certainly not Florence herself, could have foreseen the significance of the meeting.

But Florence was at once attracted and impressed by

Sidney Herbert. Who would not have been? He was thirty-seven, recently married—yes, this was in fact his bridal journey, a long holiday between sessions of Parliament in which for fifteen years, almost from the time he left Oxford, he'd had a seat. He was a descendant of Sir Philip Sidney's sister and named for that gentle knight; Lord Pembroke was his half-brother, Wilton—the finest country residence in England—his home. To date his political career had been brilliant; he was perhaps the best-known among younger English statesmen. Indeed, all the virtues seemed combined in him. He was handsome; he had a keen intellect, chivalrous manners, a charming personality.

He had something else too, which Florence Nightingale was quick to perceive—an unwavering loyalty to goodness for its own sake, a purpose like a steadily burning fire to exert all his genius for the uplifting of his fellowmen. Clasping Sidney Herbert's hand, she recognized in him the man she herself would have wished to be—had not fate cast her in woman's inferior role.

After that chance meeting, the Bracebridges, the Herberts and Florence were almost constantly together, riding, driving, seeing galleries, a congenial group never lacking subjects for discussion.

"The most entire and unbroken freedom from dreaming I ever had," Florence later called it.

Elizabeth Herbert, blonde, vivacious, much younger than her husband, urged Sidney to tell about the hospital he hoped to build.

"A hospital? Florence will just dote on that!" Charles Bracebridge exclaimed. "Hospitals are her specialty."

Sidney glanced at her and Florence blushed. "Charles is teasing. But do tell us."

"It would be an infirmary for convalescents," Sidney said. "There are thirty-two villages on the Pembroke estates, several thousand people. I want an infirmary where these people of mine can recuperate after illness and be given the most modern medical treatment in the best possible conditions."

"His plans are all down on paper," said Elizabeth proudly.

"But I've much to do before I start building." He looked again at Florence. "Since your hobby is hospitals, Miss Nightingale, perhaps you'd come to Charmouth sometime and inspect the location and plans."

"Yes, I will," she said.

"Splendid! Just as soon as we're all in England again?"

"Make it a first order of business," Elizabeth begged. "And don't forget, Florence!"

Florence smiled. She would not forget. No danger.

With the Bracebridges she returned to England in the early summer, and shortly thereafter she went to Wilton for several days with the Herberts. Together, she and Sidney bent over the draughtsman's specifications for the convalescents' hospital.

Their first consultation. It would not be their last.

If only the "unbroken freedom from dreaming" might have been permanent! But no, she was back at Embley, back in the old Slough of Despond. She had expected that those months in Rome would cure her of her restlessness—Mamma had expected it; instead, the relief was temporary. A note of desperation marked the entries in her diary: "My God! What is to become of me? Everything has been tried, foreign travel, kind friends, everything." Everything, it seemed, except the one desire of her ardent heart—work! That she could not have, and for the most absurd of reasons, because it was unsuitable, because she was a lady!

She and Sidney bent over the specifications

Despite her protestations to Mary Clarke, she was writing a good deal now. Perhaps she might even write a book, which would be largely about the position of well-bred women in society. They were utterly useless, of that she was convinced, the merest parasites. Women were not supposed to need food for their heads and hearts; only their bodies were kept nourished.

What a humiliation it was, and what a wicked waste. Domestic duties? High-sounding words, yes; but actually just bad habits. Florence enumerated these bad habits: "Answering a multitude of letters which lead to nothing, from her so-called friends, keeping herself up to the level of the world that she may furnish her quota of amusement at the breakfast table; driving out her company in the carriage." This was woman's lot. A hateful one!

Women had no time to themselves—"never a half hour in all their lives (excepting before or after anybody is up in the house) that they can call their own, without fear of offending or hurting someone." Lucky the woman who could get an odd moment in which to work at something of her own choosing! Home? It was not a hallowed place, but a place of confinement, from which the sons of the family went away as soon as they could go, and daughters married, often without love, just to escape.

Such were the thoughts seething in Florence's mind as she sat, apparently quiet, in the drawing-room at Embley or Lea Hurst, her grey eyes observing each detail: the thick-piled carpet and damask-covered chairs, the softly gleaming silver and sparkling glass, the floor polished like a mirror; a white-capped maid tiptoeing in with the coffee tray, a liveried manservant shutting in the warm candlelight—shutting out the world which held work to be done, evil to be vanquished, suffering to be assuaged. Nothing, surely, could be more deadly than a drawing-room. Unless it was the clock on the drawing-room wall, ticking, slowly ticking, monotonous, irritating, with creeping hands measuring off the hours of another long, dull evening, measuring off eternity.

"Why are you so pensive, Flo? You're not saying anything tonight."

"I'm sorry, Mamma."

She was thinking of her book. Perhaps she would entitle one of the chapters "Is God in the Drawing-Room?" She knew the answer, right enough!

Mrs. Nightingale had been reading a novel. A very attractive story, such a sweet heroine.

Florence had read the book, too. "Probably the heroine was sweet because she had no family ties, no mother to make demands upon her."

Mrs. Nightingale was astonished and resentful. She said to her husband, when Flo had gone up to bed, that she had always been afraid it was a risk to let the girls study so much. "Not that I notice any bad effects in Parthe. But Florence is so—so—"

"Oh, she will settle down, my dear. Don't worry. She'll be marrying, making some man a good wife."

Upstairs, Florence also was wondering at the contrast between herself and Parthe. How could Pop endure it? "*I* can't! I simply *can't!*"

Nor would she marry. There had been chances, of course; eligible young men who came to court her. Only one of them she had ever considered seriously. He was a man already distinguished; Mamma, Papa and Parthe approved of him and would have smiled on the match. Florence admired him—even more, she took great and increasing pleasure in his companionship, found herself leaning on his sympathy. He had proposed, she had refused him, yet he persisted.

"I could be satisfied to spend a life with him," she

wrote. Yes, she could be *happy* with him. But wouldn't such happiness be just a form of selfishness? Perhaps she would only be fleeing from one drawing-room to another quite like it? If she married, her ambition would certainly go by the board—she could not face the prospect! Work, the kind of work she wanted, was infinitely more precious than a wife's happiness. That was "the true and rich life."

She knew that this determination of hers to live and die a spinster was a disappointment to her parents—to everybody. Once, a friend of whom she was fond had remarked to another friend, "Our dear Flo has just recovered from a severe cold, but I hear nothing of what I long for, that some noble-hearted gentleman, one who can love her as she deserves to be loved, prepares to take her to a home of her own." Well, that was news which her friends would never hear! Once Aunt Mai had suggested that a husband might in certain circumstances be an advantage. Had not Elizabeth Fry been helped by the fact that there was a Mr. Fry to encourage and support her? Florence was skeptical of this argument. Let others marry if it pleased them.

Love was not for her!

Yet she liked to talk with men, to listen to them—and to know that sometimes they listened to her. Dinner conversations were easy for her; she charmed her partners by the breadth of her information, the depth of her learning. Sometimes she amazed them.

"That daughter of Nightingale's, the younger one— very clever, isn't she? Very sharp, something of a bluestocking. Gets a chap to spouting on some topic of which he thinks he knows a lot; his *favorite* topic, geology maybe, Greek inscriptions, theology, something of the

sort. Gets a chap to showing off a bit, preening himself—
and then it's Miss Florence's turn, and in a moment she's
proving that she knows far *more* about it. Well, well! A
capital young lady—if she hadn't floored me with her
Latin and Greek."

In the autumn of 1848 Florence's hopes soared suddenly to an ecstatic height. Mrs. Nightingale was going
to Carlsbad, to take the waters there, her daughters must
accompany her.

Carlsbad? Why, it was not far from Kaiserswerth.
Not *too* far, anyway. Mary Clarke was now married to
Julius Mohl, the eminent orientalist; the Mohls would
meet the Nightingale ladies in Frankfurt—

"While you all go on to the baths, I shall be off to
Kaiserswerth!" said Florence.

"Ah?" said Mamma, with lifted brows.

But it was not to be. Political troubles were brewing
in Germany; Mr. Nightingale thought the trip unsafe,
the plan was given up, and Parthenope and Florence
went with Mamma to Malvern.

Florence was bitterly chagrined. Kaiserswerth, Pastor
Fliedner, the deaconesses had seemed just within reach
—and then slipped once more into the realm of the unat-
tainable.

Seeing the shadow in her eyes, Mr. Nightingale said
that he had no objection to Florence's spending several
months in London where she might look over the hospitals and learn for herself what the nursing profession
was like. She could put up at Grandfather Smith's house,
or even in a decorous hotel; she might do a bit of charitable work in the Ragged Schools, those institutions
which attempted to reform and educate wayward

and destitute boys, gathered in from the London streets.

It was a compromise, but Florence accepted. She went to London and was briefly on the teaching staff of the Ragged Schools. Her pupils she spoke of as "my little thieves of Westminster"; they interested her. But her efforts at accomplishing much of good among them was somewhat hampered by her promise to Mamma that she would never be seen in public without an older woman or a trusted servant to convoy her. The "little thieves" responded to Miss Nightingale's cordiality—but they balked when confronted by her chaperon. The proprieties were against Florence.

Yet the months were profitable, for she was storing up quantities of information on hospitals in general, and prevailing methods of nursing. All her discoveries verified what she'd been told by the Reverend Mr. Giffard, by Papa, Mamma, everyone. Hospitals almost without exception were dirty, unsystematic, unsanitary, literally pesthouses where disease ran rampant and epidemics occurred periodically. Nurses, underpaid, recruited from the lowest classes, were often of the charwoman type; they could not read or write; they drank, stole, cheated, neglected their patients.

But whose faults were these? They must be laid at the door of a society which permitted them! They could be corrected!

Florence filled notebooks with her jottings as to how the whole lamentable situation might be revolutionized. Her scrutiny was critical, her vision clear.

Perhaps some day she would be able to do more than theorize. She existed only for that day.

7

GLIMPSE OF A MISSION

THE BRACEBRIDGES were traveling again, this time to Greece and Egypt, and nothing would do but that Florence go with them. Only think, Selina said, of all the hospitals they might see en route; and Charles added that, returning, they probably would stop in Germany.

"What do you say, Florence?" asked the Bracebridges.

She said yes. Perhaps she would have said it anyway, for the old feeling of despondency was upon her and she was particularly displeased with the drawing-room clock; but the word Germany had an unique sound, it meant the magic attraction of Kaiserswerth. Maybe now she could set foot into that land of her visioning.

So, in the autumn of 1849, Florence left Embley for another glimpse of foreign countries, and once more Parthe voiced the hope that her dear sister would find a measure of peace, saying that Egypt might do for Florence what Rome had failed to do.

Mrs. Nightingale made no comment at all. She was almost ready to acknowledge herself baffled by the peculiarities of her younger daughter.

As was her custom, Florence took a great many books with her: "learned books," Parthe called them; and, traveling, Florence bought others, which she constantly studied, storing up a vast fund of information on mythology, history and folklore. Egypt was a place of infinite wonders; and though she must deplore the backwardness of its people and their system of laws, she admired the beauty of its scenery and wrote to Parthe long letters about the temples and tombs and statues. Of course, she made the opportunity to look into any charitable institutions seen in passing; at Alexandria she spent a good deal of time with the nuns of St. Vincent de Paul in their well-kept schools and the visitors' rooms of their convents. She wrote to Parthe that there were only nineteen of these noble religieuses, but they did uncomplainingly the work of ninety. The desert also interested Florence; she liked going out alone to watch the sunset. She told Parthe that she enjoyed poking her nose into the small villages which skirted the expanses of untracked sand. "I want to see how these poor people live."

It was April when the travelers reached Greece, and a political crisis was in process; but this did not curtail Florence's sight-seeing. At Athens she viewed the Parthenon by moonlight and said that nothing earth or heaven could produce would ever excel its loveliness. One day in the ancient city, inside a ruined temple, she performed a small act of mercy, rescuing a baby owl which had fallen from its nest and been snatched up by a party of yelling (and, Florence thought, probably cruel) street urchins.

The Greek boys would not give their catch to the slender Englishwoman who demanded it; but they were willing to sell.

"A farthing," Florence said, holding out the coin. "A farthing for the owlet?"

The boys nodded and clutched at the money. The tiny

bird fluttered to the ground, and Florence stooped and picked it up and put it into her pocket.

Selina Bracebridge, who had witnessed the purchase, was amused. "What now, Florence?"

"This is Athena," Florence said, "and she is going with us all the way. I shall take her in my pocket as a present for Parthe, who will simply adore her."

"But you have a cicada as a traveling occupant of your pocket," said Selina.

"Yes. I suppose Athena may eat the cicada. Well, it will only be the consolidating of two pets in one, and just imagine how happy Athena will be at Embley where there are oceans of mice to be had for the hunting."

Laughing, Selina said she feared that Athena was too much an infant to hunt as yet; but Florence, nothing daunted, said that Mamma's butler could provide the mice until Athena had grown old enough to feed herself.

Perhaps Florence's keenest pleasure in Athens was the time spent with American missionaries who conducted a school and orphanage there. Yet this had its depressing side, too. How worthless seemed her own existence when contrasted with that of the women missionaries. The thought greatly vexed her, and Selina Bracebridge felt that an attack of fever which Florence suffered just then was largely brought on by worry over what Florence described as her uselessness.

"Well," Selina said, "we shall soon be in Berlin; the hospitals in the German capital will lure you from the doldrums."

Florence did not reply, but thought that she wouldn't tarry long in Berlin, however fascinating were the hospitals. The distance from Berlin to Kaiserswerth was comparatively short, and from the moment of leaving England, Kaiserswerth had been her real destination.

July 31, a memorable day indeed, for Florence was at last in the little Prussian town, actually entering Pastor Fliedner's famous establishment, meeting the good man face-to-face. She wrote in her diary: "I could hardly believe I was there. With the feeling with which a pilgrim first looks on the Kedron, I saw the Rhine, dearer to me than the Nile." She was to stay a fortnight; the question was, she thought, how best to crowd into that brief interval all the many things she wished to learn.

Pastor Fliedner made her welcome and showed her over his buildings which now comprised a hospital of a hundred beds, an infant school, a penitentiary with twelve inmates, an orphan asylum and a normal school where school mistresses were trained. There was also the training school for nurses, housing a hundred deaconesses. Florence was given a blue cotton habit and a white apron, the deaconess' uniform which she donned proudly.

It seemed that cleanliness was the first lesson in the Kaiserswerth course for beginners; they scrubbed the floors.

"But you, Miss Nightingale, will not wish to scrub," said Pastor Fliedner, with a glance for Florence's well-groomed white hands which had never known such hard work.

Certainly she wished to scrub! Fetching soap and water, she got down on the floor and, with his eyes humorously upon her, she wielded the heavy brush. Finishing, she stood up, brushed her dark hair from her forehead and waited for him to speak.

"A very dirty floor, Miss Nightingale," he said, "and you have scrubbed it until it shines."

She wielded the heavy brush

She smiled, feeling strangely close to tears, as if she had won some knightly accolade.

A busy fortnight; and oh, such a happy one. "The world here fills my life with interest," wrote Florence to her mother. "We have ten minutes for each of our meals, of which we have four. We get up at five; breakfast a quarter before six. The patients dine at eleven; the sisters at twelve. We drink tea, that is, a drink made of ground rye, between two and three, and sup at seven. Several evenings in the week we collect in the great hall for a Bible lesson." Herr Fliedner's wisdom and knowledge of human nature were, she said, inspiring. "This is life. Now I know what it is to love life."

She did not add the thought so often in her mind—that here birth, breeding, station were as nothing and all that mattered was the willingness to work for others. Had Florence Nightingale been the lowliest commoner, Pastor Fliedner could not have accepted her presence more calmly. The deaconesses were entirely matter-of-fact, cool, kind, impersonal in their attitude toward this newcomer. If there was about her some odd distinction as, in her blue and white garments, she moved among them, they disregarded it. To them she was just another woman wanting to help. In their humble and self-effacing service of God, through the least of His creatures, she found the fulfillment of a desire long thwarted.

Only a fortnight of this deeply satisfying happiness—and then she must rejoin the Bracebridges who had been at Düsseldorf. But the riches gained could never be taken from her, and she knew that some day she would come back. "Left Kaiserswerth," she recorded in the diary, "feeling so brave, as if nothing could ever vex me again."

With her friends she went to Ghent and in a week she was writing out in pamphlet form her observations of Pastor Fliedner's accomplishments. The Bracebridges said they would remain in Ghent until she had completed her manuscript.

"Shall you publish it, Florence?" asked Selina.

"Yes, anonymously, when I'm in England."

She had no intention of publicizing her own experiences, but she wanted British readers to know about *The Institution of Kaiserswerth on the Rhine.*

By the end of August she was at home.

As she had predicted, Parthe greeted the little owl Athena with exclamations of delight, and apparently Athena was just as enthusiastic about her new mistress and Embley—where the butler was most obliging at foraging for young mice.

"You have tamed Athena so nicely," said Parthe to Florence, "that she sleeps regularly in my lap and can balance herself on my shoulder when I walk around. And her manners are charming!"

But a few weeks later this opinion of Athena's manners had to be temporarily revised. One morning Parthe came downstairs wearing a ruffled cap over her hair— just an ordinary white cap, but Athena, perched on the mantel, did not like it. With a hoarse cry and a flap of wings, the owl darted toward Parthe, seized a ruffled edge of the cap in her beak and twitched it off. Then Athena retreated to the mantel, sulking.

"Oh, you naughty bird," said Parthe, laughing. "You seem not a bit afraid of me. Perhaps you're not afraid of anything."

But this was another opinion which had to be revised. Some guest at Embley had given Mrs. Nightingale a large china owl in which a lighted candle could be set, the glow of the candle illuminating the green glass eyes of the china figure. At her first glimpse of this imitation of herself, Athena was resentful and frightened, and when Parthe put her down in front of those glittering eyes, she uttered shrieks of protest and flew away to the protection of the darkened drawing-room.

"She is mostly very sweet-tempered, though," Parthe said, "and I shall write her biography."

So Parthe took pen and ink and paper and started the life story of *Athena—an Owlet from the Parthenon.*

Neither the author nor the subject of this lively biography ever dreamed that the manuscript would be preserved as a precious exhibit in the British Museum Library because of its connection with the life of Florence Nightingale.

8

FIRST FREEDOM

"I AM THIRTY, the age at which Christ began His mission. Now no more childish things, no more vain things, no more love, no more marriage. Now, Lord, let me only think of Thy will."

This and other equally serious notations in Florence's 1850 diary betrayed the period of her very worst discouragement. She seemed out of tune with all her surroundings, the gulf separating her from her mother and Parthe was ever wider, and even dear Papa was disturbed by her behavior, the things she said and did—the things she could not avoid saying and doing!

She had never known a happy time, she reflected, except at Rome and at Kaiserswerth. "It is not the unhappiness I mind; it is not indeed; but people can't be unhappy without making those about them so. The thoughts and feelings that I have now I can remember since I was six. A profession, a trade, a necessary occupation, something to employ all my faculties, I have always felt essential to me. The first thought I can remember, and the last, was nursing work; and in the absence of this, education work, but more the education of the bad than of the young."

After numerous drawing-room ordeals, she wrote, "Oh, weary days, O evenings that seem never to end!

For how many long years I have watched that clock and thought it would never reach the ten. And for twenty or thirty more to do this!" Occasionally she would contrive to put forward the hands of the torturing clock, and flee a few minutes early from the family circle. "O how am I to get through this day," she asked herself each morning, "to talk through all this day? Why do I wish to leave this world? God knows I do not expect a heaven beyond, but that He would set me down in St. Giles', at a Kaiserswerth, there to find my work and my salvation in my work."

Yet in the midst of despair, she had recurrent flashes of rebellion. "I must *take* some things, as few as I can, to enable me to live. I must take them, they will not be given me." Silently she was arming for the break which must surely come; she would abandon hope of ever obtaining her mother's or Parthe's understanding, but she would try to hurt them as little as possible.

As for marriage, upon which she turned her back, she had years ago ruled against that, and it irritated her that Mamma, and even Papa, should still speak of it. Florence argued that she was now too old to marry; but Mamma said Pshaw! she herself had been thirty when she married William Shore Nightingale, and then she had chosen a husband six years her junior. Why, thirty was just a good age for marrying, and there were plenty of young bachelors who would bask in Florence's smile.

"No," Florence said. "No, please don't think of it."

At length she convinced her father of her absolute rejection of marriage, and with him she made a quaint sort of compact. "If," she pointed out, "I haven't changed my views within two more years, if at thirty-two I am still single, I shall deserve the same privileges you would have granted a grown son. Won't you let me lead then the kind of life I want?"

Rather anxiously Mr. Nightingale said he supposed so, for he had also been listening to his sister Mai, who had interceded in Florence's behalf. Yes, and he would settle an allowance on his dear Flo, because she must not feel poverty-stricken.

Florence thanked him. The compact would not be put down on paper, she said. "But I should like to call in Selina Bracebridge, Papa, and have her know the terms, so that she can vouch for my freedom, if it should ever be questioned."

After that, Florence somehow looked upon Papa as an ally and talked to him of how she should train and prepare herself for the future. Mrs. Nightingale and Parthe were going to Carlsbad for three months—it would be a chance, Florence said, for her to go to Kaiserswerth again.

"Very well," said Mr. Nightingale.

But as might have been expected, his wife was vigorously opposed. Bad enough, cried Mrs. Nightingale, that Florence should have published that pamphlet on Pastor Fliedner's project; many Britishers had guessed its authorship. Now if it were known that Florence was again at Kaiserswerth, for such a long time, three whole months, actually nursing in the hospital—what on earth would people *say*? Mrs. Nightingale cared terribly what people said, while Florence cared not at all.

"Why need anyone know, Mamma? I'll not mention it, if you don't."

"Nothing could prevail upon *me* to mention it. You think we might conceal your going from *everybody*?"

"Like the shameful thing it is? Yes, Mamma," replied Florence.

But concealment was a snare and a delusion, and after Mrs. Nightingale had entrenched herself in Carlsbad with Parthe and was drinking the waters, a letter from Florence said that the secret was out. It was all quite mysterious and not Florence's doing, but a few people did know that she was at Kaiserswerth. The Sidney Herberts, who were at Homburg, had paid her a visit. Refusing to think that Mamma could be really offended, Florence wrote often and lovingly of how busy she was—"until yesterday I never had time even to send my clothes to the wash"—of how she had taken the convalescent boys for beautiful walks in the country; how she was strengthened in body and heart.

"I know you will be glad to hear this, dearest Mum."

Mrs. Nightingale sighed, and was not glad.

Finally Florence wrote a long letter, appealing for her "beloved people's" sympathy.

Mrs. Nightingale was mute, having no sympathy to extend.

"Don't fret, Mamma," said Parthe. "As well that Flo is having this little fling; we can the sooner get her back to Lea Hurst."

Mrs. Nightingale wrote to the Mohls in Paris that she hoped "our dear child Florence" would be able to apply all the fine learning she had been acquiring—"to do a little to make us better. Parthe is much too idle to help and too apt to be satisfied with things as they are."

This second stay at Kaiserswerth was a milestone in Florence's life, everything which followed must be dated from those three months. Though she went docilely back to the leisure of Lea Hurst and Embley, she was bolder, much more assured, biding her time and knowing that she would eventually escape. Many of her friends in London were persons of prestige and influence: George Eliot, Elizabeth Barrett Browning, Lady Lovelace, who was Lord Byron's daughter. All were impressed with her intelligence, her air of quiet competence. "An earnest, noble woman," they called her, believing that she would some day achieve her ambitions. Lady Lovelace wrote a poem about her, the last stanza of which would be remembered later as an example of amazing prediction:

> "In future years, in distant climes,
>   Should war's dread strife its victims claim,
>   Should pestilence, unchecked betimes,
>   Strike more than sword, than cannon maim,
>   He who then reads these truthful rhymes
>   Will trace her progress to undying fame."

In hours which would otherwise have been empty, Florence endeavored to formulate her rather unorthodox religious creed, writing it all out and then discussing what she had written with Papa, who had a taste for such self-analysis. She modestly titled these essays *Suggestions for Thought*.

"Shall we have your book printed, Florence?" asked Papa.

"Not now," she said. "Perhaps in a few years I'll print it privately."

According to the compact, she was to be permitted at thirty-two to start on her career—the nature of which was still vague, though certainly it would be some type of nursing. Therefore in the summer of 1852 she told Papa that she was going to Paris, where she would study in various Catholic orphanages and hospitals. But her mother had by no means sanctioned the compact, nor had she conceded defeat.

"You cannot travel alone, Florence. That I will not have!"

Florence said that Hilary Bonham Carter was going with her; the two younger women would travel with Lady Augusta Bruce, who was a lady-in-waiting to the Queen.

"Ah?" murmured Mrs. Nightingale, and for a week or two said nothing more. But then there was news that Florence's Great-aunt Evans was very ill. The journey *must* be postponed. "You would not be disrespectful to Great-aunt Evans, Florence?"

No, the trip would be postponed, Florence said, until Great-aunt Evans had improved.

Mrs. Nightingale made the most of the delay. "My dear, if you will give up Paris entirely, you may have that little old house on your father's Derbyshire estate—Cromford Bridge House—and convert it into a small hospital all your own. Doesn't that tempt you?"

"No," Florence said. "A small hospital of my own is not what I want now, Mamma. I am really going to Paris."

She went—and a letter from Mrs. Nightingale recalled her. Grandmamma Shore was sick again at Tapton, she begged for Florence. "You must come home and nurse her in her last illness."

Wearily Florence returned to England, to Tapton. It was in truth Grandmamma Shore's last illness; she was ninety-five and after a few weeks she died.

"You will have to assist with the funeral, Florence!"

"Yes, Mamma, I will."

She assisted with the funeral, and then repacked her trunk.

"Florence, you're not going back to France?"

"Yes, Mamma."

Mrs. Nightingale dissolved in tears. "Oh, please, my dear!"

"I am sorry if it grieves you, but I can't change the plan. I shall visit the Mohls in Paris. You are fond of them. You can trust them to protect me."

Mrs. Nightingale said sadly that she had always thought charity began at home.

In Paris again, Florence methodically set about her study, inspecting infirmaries and convents, seeing the work done by those of Pastor Fliedner's deaconesses who were nursing in France. She collected reports and statistics and compiled statistics where none had been before; she observed Paris surgeons in their clinics, she read case histories in medical libraries.

Every day, from morning to night, she was out, glorying in her sense of liberation, of being answerable only to herself. She was all over the city, in every nook and cranny, scorning to take a cab, instead riding on the omnibuses, rubbing elbows with the commonest folk—and how distressed Mamma would have been to know! In the evenings she could, if she wished, attend the social functions to which her host and hostess, Professor and Madame Mohl, were constantly invited and eager to escort her.

It was in Paris, the spring of 1853, that she was offered her first post of responsibility. The letter was from London. At 8 Chandos Street, Cavendish Square, the Establishment for Gentlewomen during Illness, which provided a home for sick governesses and other invalids or super-annuated ladies of the "gentlewomen" class, was in need of a new superintendent. Miss Nightingale had been recommended. Would she accept?

Well, not at once. "It isn't precisely what I've wanted," Florence said to Madame Mohl, "but can I afford to be too critical?"

"I think you should take it," said Madame Mohl.

"Yes, so do I. I shall send a letter of acceptance."

The Establishment for Gentlewomen! How vividly Florence would remember her year there. Mr. Sidney Herbert was on the board, probably it was he who had proposed Florence's name—and had all the other board members been as level-headed as was Mr. Herbert, the new superintendent might have been spared much quibbling. But, alas, Florence found herself saddled with a committee of directors, most of whom were ladies of wealth and exalted rank looking jealously on their pet charity and suspiciously at Miss Nightingale.

"The Society of Fashionable Asses." That was the nickname Florence had for the committee; and in letters to Madame Mohl she told, with the sharpness and sarcasm which often tinged her pen, how she coped with them, skirmishing to get the upper hand.

"If you knew what the 'fashionable asses' have been doing, their 'offs' and their 'ons,' poor fools! There are no surgeon students nor improper patients at all, which is, of course, a great recommendation in the eyes of the Proper. The patients, or rather the Impatients, for I know what it is to nurse sick ladies, are all pay patients, poor friendless folk in London. I am to have the choosing of the house, the appointment of the Chaplain and the management of the funds as the F. S. A. are *at present* minded. But Isaiah himself could not prophesy how they will be minded at 8 o'clock this evening."

"The choosing of the house?" That meant the immediate moving of the institution from Chandos Street to Harley Street, and was an initial victory for Florence, who had insisted upon enlarged quarters. In ten days she accomplished the tremendous undertaking. But once installed at the Harley Street address, she faced other problems which bobbed up with astonishing rapidity.

A nursing home, Florence said, must have modern conveniences, such as bells ringing to summon the nurses, and an elevator, "a lift, in order that the nurse might not be merely a pair of legs." The committee had to be persuaded to these innovations, for there had been no bells or lift in Chandos Street.

Then Florence said that the rule forbidding the superintendent to walk with the doctors on their rounds must be revoked. Since she had been hired to assume full charge of the building, she would demand access to every part of it—yes, even to the operating room when surgery was in progress. The ladies of the committee were horrified. Only after debate would they assent, and then grudgingly.

But the knottiest problem concerned religion. The institution was Protestant, always had been, and must remain so. No Catholic patients, said the committee, could be admitted.

Miss Nightingale was instantly resentful. If that was the spirit of the place, she would have nothing to do with it—nothing! She would politely wish the committee good morning and withdraw. This issue was threshed out at prodigious length, while Florence stood firm.

Finally the committee agreed to lower the bars to Catholic patients.

"I shall take in Jews too," said Florence, who had no tolerance for any intolerance.

The committee bowed to her imperious edict

The committee groaned. "Not Jews?"

"Yes," said Florence, never budging an inch.

The committee bowed to her imperious edict.

Though frequently irritated, the new superintendent could laugh at her troubles. She seemed to have become a buffer between the "fashionable asses" and the staff of doctors—and out of favor with them all. But she learned to manipulate these factions, cleverly posing them one against the other, putting ideas into their heads, words into their mouths, and then letting them think that the ideas and the words had originated with themselves.

So, with somewhat the wiliness of the politician, she got things done, reducing friction to a minimum and seeking no credit or praise. The institution soon ran smoothly, and the inmates loved their efficient Miss Nightingale.

Florence often wrote to her father, telling him of her work; at his request, she sent the letters to Mr. Nightingale's London club. She did not correspond with her mother or Parthe, for the fact was that relations with them were more strained than ever. Mrs. Nightingale had hated the thought of Flo's being a superintendent—it was really dreadful! But if Florence just *would* be so queer, at least she could live with her family when the Nightingales came to London for the season. How much more comfortable she would be in a nice hotel than in that old asylum, or whatever it was.

Florence said no. At long, long last she was independent; the break she had made was "not likely to be repented of or reconsidered."

"But will you not come to Lea Hurst for a vacation this summer, Flo?" implored Parthe.

Florence said yes, and went for a few days in August, cutting short her holiday because of hearing that an epidemic of cholera threatened London. Hastening back to Harley Street, she looked out not only for her governesses but also for many cholera patients in the Middle-sex Hospital. The epidemic subsided in the early autumn —and then it was that the interest of all London, and all England, and a great portion of the wide world centered suddenly upon incidents of the Crimean War, and Florence Nightingale heard the call of her particular and magnificent destiny.

9

THE CALL TO SERVICE

THE WAR WAS ONE which most observers (and eminent English historians among them) would have great difficulty explaining and justifying. The surface cause was Russia's policy of expansion and the wish of England to join with France in preventing the further encroachment of the Czar's armies upon Turkish territory. But the hidden and real cause was the age-old fear of nations that another nation may surpass it in power and conquest. In 1853 Russia had mobilized and occupied the portion of Turkey lying north of the Danube River; Russia had attacked and destroyed a Turkish squadron—very daringly, within sight of French and British warships stationed in the Bosporus. These acts seemed a challenge which England and France must answer with a declaration of war.

The campaigns which followed, on land and sea, were notable chiefly for their lack of military skill, the blundering of officials, the senseless sacrifice of troops and, finally, a peace in which it was realized that little of worth had been accomplished.

Early in 1854, to defend Turkey, England and France had dispatched an expeditionary force to Varna, a port on the Black Sea, fifty-seven thousand men, the largest body of troops ever sent to do battle on foreign soil.

When Russia saw this force, she edged away, dodging the fight. At about the same time, it became evident that the English and French soldiers must not be left at Varna because cholera raged there. Then the defending armies were somehow obliged to attack, instead. An invasion of the Crimean peninsula was decided upon, and Lord Raglan went out from England to command the Queen's men.

The first major engagement of the war was the Battle of Alma, which occurred September 20, 1854, six days after the landing of the British and French in the Crimea, and it was the result of this battle which so abruptly shocked England to what was happening in that far-off area—where, until now, things had seemed so slow, so uneventful and almost dull. Her Majesty's troops had been victorious; that is, they had fought with their usual brilliance and had taken their objective—but at a terrible cost! Even while England exulted in news of the triumph, the casualty lists began to arrive. So many brave men killed or wounded! Even worse were the reports of soldiers dying out there, dying by the hundreds, dying of neglect, because proper care was denied them, because medical supplies, good food, doctors and nurses had not been provided in sufficient amount—had, in fact, scarcely been provided at all!

William Howard Russell had gone to the Crimea as "special correspondent" for the London *Times*. He was an able newspaperman, his present mission was a novel one, for until he undertook the task, a "special correspondent" with an army in the field was a thing unknown. Mr. Russell with his own eyes had seen the Battle of Alma and its sad aftermath of needless suffering; he wrote back uncensored letters to the *Times*, which when printed made the country gasp with horror and remorse.

"It is with feelings of surprise and anger that the public will learn that no sufficient preparations have been made

Soldiers were dying of neglect

for the proper care of the wounded," wrote Mr. Russell. "Not only are there not sufficient surgeons—that, it might be urged, was unavoidable; not only are there no dressers and nurses—that might be a defect of system for which no one is to blame; but what will be said when it is known that there is not even linen to make bandages for the wounded?"

The Turks had turned over to the British a huge building in Scutari, which was a suburb of Constantinople, a building called the Barrack Hospital and here the wounded were being housed—as many of them, anyway, as survived the voyage from the Crimea to Turkey. But, mostly, the wounded died during the three hundred mile trip across the Black Sea, "expiring in agony," Mr. Russell said, "unheeded and shaken off, though catching desperately at the surgeon whenever he makes his rounds through the fetid ship." Those who lived to reach Scutari and the Barrack Hospital found themselves, with week-old wounds never touched by the hand of a medical man, shunted rudely into a cold, bare, echoing place where, as Mr. Russell said, "the commonest appliances of a workhouse sick ward are wanting," where "the men must die through the medical staff of the British army having forgotten that old rags are necessary for the dressing of wounds."

Mr. Russell had not misjudged the reaction of his public. His letters, appearing every day, were sensational, instantly arousing a storm of questions as to why these conditions prevailed. No nurses? Well, only a handful of very old pensioners, feeble old fellows who had been sent as an "ambulance corps," and were so far past the age for usefulness that they died themselves or fell sick and needed nursing. No hospital supplies? None, said Mr. Russell emphatically. "For all I can observe, these men die without the least effort being made to save them. There they lie, just as they were let down on the ground by their poor comrades, who brought them on their backs from the camp with the greatest tenderness, but who are not allowed to remain with them. The sick seem to be tended by the sick, and the dying by the dying."

Amid general indignation and excitement on the part of his readers, Mr. Russell's letters continued, "It is now pouring rain, the skies are black as ink, the wind is howling. Our men have not either warm or waterproof clothing . . . not a soul seems to care for their comfort, or even for their lives. These are hard truths, but the people of England must hear them. They must know that the wretched beggar who wanders about the streets of London leads the life of a prince compared with the British soldiers who are fighting out here for their country."

Of course, something must be done! At once! But what?

Mr. Russell drew a sharp contrast between his government and the French, "Their medical arrangements are extremely good, their surgeons more numerous, and they have the help of the Sisters of Charity who have accompanied the expedition. These devoted women are excellent nurses."

Well, why had not England some Sisters of Charity? The question had its first public asking in the *Times* of October 14. "There are numbers of ablebodied and tender-hearted Englishwomen who would joyfully and with alacrity go out to devote themselves to nursing the sick and wounded if they could be associated for that purpose and placed under proper protection." Once thrust forward, the query resounded the length and breadth of the British Isles. *"If nurses are needed, why can't we send them?"*

Then, in the minds of a few persons, a more explicit suggestion stirred. Henry Edward Manning (afterward Cardinal) wrote to the Bishop of Southwark to see if any sisters could be found for the East. "Why," said he, "will not Florence Nightingale give herself to this great work?" Already Lady Maria Forester had spoken to Miss Nightingale, if she would take out three nurses to Scutari, Lady Maria would pay all expenses of the group.

Perhaps Florence had been the very first to entertain this wonderful idea. After the most serious thought for the practical angles involved, she wrote from Harley Street on October 14 to Mrs. Sidney Herbert, her intimate friend whom she addressed as "My dearest," expressing her wish to go to Turkey, requesting Mrs. Herbert to lay the matter before her husband. There would be, Florence knew, many details to be smoothed out, permissions, grants of authority, official consents and credentials to be obtained—but she was anxious, indeed determined, to go, whether sponsored by the government or as a private agent, because "I do believe that we may be of use to the wounded wretches."

This letter to Elizabeth Herbert crossed in the mails a letter which Sidney Herbert had posted to Florence from Bournemouth, October 15, where he was spending the Sunday. Knowing nothing of Florence's inclinations, but pondering deeply, Mr. Herbert had come to the conclusion that there was just one way to remedy the lamentable situation. Nurses must be sent, they must be strictly supervised and directed—and Miss Nightingale was the only person in England who would be capable of organizing and superintending such a scheme.

His letter was very long and reasoned, for he had deliberated over every phase of it. He was quite aware that what he asked was amazing, even revolutionary— "none but male nurses having ever been admitted to military hospitals." He felt that Mr. Russell's stories were perhaps a bit exaggerated, for medical stores had been shipped to the Crimea in profusion, "by the *ton* weight;" and doctors had gone in the proportion of one to every ninety-five men. As to what had become of these tons of stores, these doctors, he could not surmise, but he was hopeful of their arrival. Still, the crying need was for nurses.

"I do not say one word to press you. You can judge for yourself which of conflicting or incompatible duties is the first, or the highest; but I must not conceal from you that I think upon your decision will depend the ultimate success or failure of the plan. Your own personal qualities, your knowledge and your power of administration, and among greater things your rank and position in Society give you the advantages in such a work which no other person possesses."

The government, Mr. Herbert said, would stanchly co-operate, the entire medical staff would be sworn to fullest assistance, everything requisite to the mission would be furnished in unlimited abundance. "I know you will come to a wise decision. God grant it may be in accordance with my hopes!"

Florence received Sidney Herbert's letter one day and, so swiftly did events trend, the very next day it was proclaimed from the War Office that Miss Nightingale, "a lady with greater practical experience of hospital administration and treatment than any other lady in the country," had been appointed by the Government as Superintendent of Nurses at Scutari, and had begun her work of organization as a preface to sailing for Turkey.

"Who is Florence Nightingale?"
That was now the question. Through the years, through

the prominence of her family, Florence had made a wide circle of friends, but she had never been a public figure. Overnight she had become the most talked-of person in England, the focus for national attention, her name on everyone's lips.

"Who *is* she? Tell us something *about* our heroine!"

Well, the newspapers could do that, and they got their information from the most reliable sources—from Mrs. Nightingale and from Parthe. Suddenly all conflict and stress in what had been at best an unsatisfactory relationship was forgotten; with pride Mamma and Parthe had spoken of the honor bestowed upon Florence, and had even displayed the War Office's letter to inquiring reporters. Mamma declared that she and Mr. Nightingale were ducks who had miraculously hatched a swan. Parthe said of dear Flo that "the way in which all things have tended to and fitted her for this is so very remarkable that one cannot but believe she was intended for it."

The *Examiner* and then the *Times* printed articles. Miss Nightingale was "a young lady of singular endowments, both natural and acquired. In a knowledge of the ancient languages and of the higher branches of mathematics, in general art, science and literature, her attainments are extraordinary. There is scarcely a modern language which she does not understand, and she speaks French, German and Italian as fluently as her native English. She has visited and studied all the various nations of Europe and has ascended the Nile to its remotest cataract. Young (about the age of our Queen), graceful, feminine, rich, popular, she holds a singularly gentle and persuasive influence over all with whom she comes in contact. Her friends and acquaintances are of all classes and persuasions, but her happiest place is at home, in the centre of a very large band of accomplished relatives, and in simplest obedience to her admiring parents."

Florence, if she read the articles, must have smiled rather ironically. Her happiest place at home? Her simple obedience to admiring parents? Picturesque, yes; but hardly exact. The newspapers, in a well-meant flood of enthusiasm, persisted in dwelling upon the sacrifice made by this charming and sensitive young lady, with her background of exalted birth and breeding, how she was forsaking assemblies, lectures, concerts, exhibitions and all the social pleasures of taste and intellect to which she was accustomed. Sacrifice? Absurd! thought Florence. The only thing in life she had ever desired was service of just the kind which was now at hand. It was what a little girl in the chapel at Lea Hurst had dreamed of, it was the very stuff of dreams and long suppressed yearnings.

It was opportunity—at last! And she had seized it!

10

JOURNEY AND ARRIVAL

"THE SELECTION OF NURSES, the finding of women equal to a task full of horrors and requiring, besides knowledge and good will, great energy and great courage, will be very difficult," Sidney Herbert had said to Florence.

He was quite right. There were but a few days for this business; even in the moment of her appointment Florence had shouldered a tremendous burden.

Her temporary headquarters were at Mr. Herbert's house, 49 Belgrave Square. An appeal for volunteers had gone forth, and here Florence interviewed all applicants. She was aided by Mrs. Bracebridge and another friend, Miss Mary Stanley; and often Parthe was present, sorting and packaging the vast quantities of knitted socks and shirts, the linen for bandages, which poured in from contributors throughout the Kingdom.

Parthe marveled at her sister's restrained manner. "In the midst of all this furious tumult and haste, you are calm as a May morning, Flo! You behave as if you were going, not to war, but just out for a walk in the park!"

Florence smiled. "What is there to be perturbed about?"

"Well, the War Office, the Military Medical Board, and half the nurses in London are waiting their turn to consult with you."

"Everything is moving nicely though, Pop—thanks to

my helpers. And everyone is so kind, rallying to a national emergency."

"Rallying to *you*," said Parthe generously. "Because you have fired the public's imagination as it never was fired before!"

Florence would have had to be much less clever than she was, not to see truth in this statement, and her heart was touched by the loyalty she encountered everywhere. Mr. and Mrs. Herbert were unwavering in her support; the Bracebridges had said they were going to Scutari, too; Uncle Sam Smith declared he would go as far as Marseilles; Aunt Mai had promised to respond to any demand Florence might make upon her time and effort. The people in the London streets were positive that Miss Nightingale was a saint who would soon have all the wounded British soldiers up and on their feet again. Nothing was too good for Miss Nightingale! Nothing was good *enough*!

Florence had thought of taking nineteen nurses with her, a party of twenty in all; but Mr. Herbert said there should be more. Forty was the number agreed upon, and now Florence must enroll them. She did not lack material; as Parthe had said, half the nurses in London seemed to be clamoring at the gates, besides scores of other women who had never before in their lives given a thought to nursing. But much of this material fell short of the standards Florence had set; the applicants must be carefully examined and weeded out, for she would have only the best.

In a small, quiet room of Mr. Herbert's house, she talked long and gravely with each volunteer.

"If," said Miss Mary Stanley, "anybody is disposed to criticize the nurses Florence accepts, I wish that person could see those she turns away. I didn't know there *were* such women! Money is what they're after, the only inducement. Just one has said she wanted to go because of a noble motive."

Parthe's comment was that Florence would choose well. "She'll not be concerned about their religions or their stations in society. Roman Catholics, Anglicans, Presbyterians—they are all the same to her; and she would every bit as soon have women of the laboring class as a lot of duchesses. What she desires is a group including all shades of opinion—just so the members will work together harmoniously and love God."

Meanwhile, Florence was not signing on her list the names of any duchesses; and several of the names sounded, and were, distinctly commonplace. When she found that further investigation would be but a waste of time, she notified Mr. Herbert of the list's closing. She had thirty-eight nurses and would see no more volunteers. For the most part, the thirty-eight were professionals, either Roman Catholics or Anglican nuns who were trained for their task.

Special Correspondent Russell had not ceased to send in his pitiful stories of the situation at Scutari, which seemed to go from bad to worse, and Florence felt that delay would be fatal. She had her own light luggage assembled, the Bracebridges and Mr. Sam Smith were ready, the accepted nurses anxious to be off. On October 21, the War Office announced that Miss Nightingale and her party would start that evening from London and would sail October 27 from Marseilles on the *Vectis*.

Only a few people came to bid the expedition farewell. Mamma and Papa were there, Parthe, the Herberts, a dozen or so of Florence's dearest friends. A still, cool autumn night, and everyone rather silent, eyes fixed on the expedition's leader, who stood tall, dignified and self-confident, well-groomed and dressed with simple elegance. As the train whistled a warning and good-byes were said, Florence kissed her parents and her sister and climbed aboard. She shed no tears, but smiled and waved her gloved hand.

She was very happy.

Mr. Sam Smith, writing home, said it probably was to be expected that confusions should arise, many arrangements be made "to keep forty in good humour." But Flo was most diplomatic with her flock. "She bears all wonderfully, winning everybody." Wherever she appeared, said Mr. Smith, there was nothing but admiration from high and low; the nurses already were quite in love with her and, because of her, were liking the journey.

When the steam packet on which they crossed the Channel came into the Boulogne harbor on the morning of October 22, the quay was thronged, for rumor of Miss Nightingale and her nurses had reached France and the populace of Boulogne wished to see and greet them. The scene was one of noise and gay color, and as Florence stepped ashore, she was surrounded by peasantwomen wearing crimson petticoats, bright kerchiefs and snowy caps like white-winged birds.

"Welcome, welcome, *les soeurs anglaises!*"

In a frenzy of excitement and joy, they surged forward, cheering these brave souls who were going out, as their own nurses had done, to a mission of mercy. Then other figures, husky, black-coated, yet feminine were pushing toward the travelers, snatching up the English bags, boxes and trunks, which they carried up the slope.

The women porters of Boulogne, and refusing to let Florence pay them, spurning almost with violence the fee she held out to them. *"Non!* You owe nothing. *Vive les soeurs!"*

Peasants and porters in attendance, the English party went to a hotel, where the landlord, the waitresses and chambermaids would not be paid or tipped, and the cheering was unabated. When the train left for Paris, Florence looked from her window at the grinning, gesticulating crowd.

"Au 'voir! Godspeed!"

There was a brief rest at Paris, then on to Marseilles. Florence purchased a great amount of stores in the French port. Though Sidney Herbert thought surely the supplies sent out from London would now be waiting at Constantinople, and though Dr. Andrew Smith, head of the Army Medical Department had said stoutly (and a little angrily) that the troops at Scutari lacked for nothing—nothing at all!—Florence had her doubts. Better to be on the safe side; and she had money with which to buy the things, food, beds, blankets, mattresses, medicines; her own money and sums donated by many patriotic Britishers.

The *Vectis* sailed as scheduled, October 27. It was a small, old-fashioned, uncomfortable vessel, but seaworthy, riding out storms, plowing doggedly through mountainous waves. Only a half-dozen of Florence's nurses had ever voyaged before; everybody else was frightened and seasick. Florence herself, normally a good sailor, felt none too well. In a letter to her parents and Parthe ("Dearest People") she told of her relief when, November 4, the ship dropped anchor at Constantinople:

"At six o'clock yesterday I staggered on deck to look at the plains of Troy, the tomb of Achilles, the mouths of the Scamander, the little harbour of Tenedos, between which and the main shore our *Vectis,* with stewards' cabins and galley torn away, blustering, creaking, shrieking, rushed on her way. We reached Constantinople this morn in a thick and heavy rain. Bad news from Balaclava. You will hear the awful wreck of our poor cavalry, four hundred wounded, arriving at this moment for us to nurse. (Later) Just starting for Scutari. We are to be housed in the hospital this very afternoon. Everybody is most kind. The wounded are, I believe, to be placed under our care. They are landing them now."

Finishing her letter, Florence went up again on deck, standing at the rail, scanning all that was visible of Constantinople. The harbor, known as the Golden Horn, was long and narrow, with the city curled around it, a city so large that it overflowed in three directions. Here, on twin banks of the Horn, were Stamboul and Galata; vast, uneven expanses of roofs and spires and minarets which thrust upward through the clinging gray mist of a chill, wet day. There, facing the Bosporus, lay Scutari, the Silver City which the Greeks had venerated, studded and wreathed with cypress trees, surmounted by domed hills; and, topping the tallest hill, the immense yellow quadrangle of the Barrack Hospital, with its square towers on four corners.

Gazing at that distant splotch of yellow among the hazy, drifting curtains of the mist, Florence thought of it as her domain, her sphere, toward which God had shown her the long, devious path. She was not afraid— no, her spirit did not falter, but was invincible as a blade of polished steel.

They were still landing the Balaclava wounded, a sorrowful procession straggling past below the rail of the *Vectis*. The world knew now what that battle had been.

The British attack upon the Russians' impregnable fortifications at Sevastopol, the charge of the Light Cavalry Brigade. With incredible gallantry, with the most foolhardy judgment, the Brigade had struck full-tilt, riding straight at the Russian artillery which was lined up, waiting, cannon yawning—and plenty of ammunition. The episode was as spectacular and fantastic as any ever to be chronicled in English military annals. It was an intrepid mass suicide which Alfred, Lord Tennyson would celebrate in verse. The Brigade had galloped, the Russian guns boomed—the Light Cavalry was slashed to ribbons, crushed, reduced to this litter of broken bodies carried on canvas stretchers.

> "Stormed at with shot and shell,
>   Boldly they rode and well;
>   Into the jaws of Death,
>   Into the mouth of Hell,
>   Rode the six hundred."

"Miss Nightingale?"

Florence turned from her thoughts of Balaclava's immortal slaughter. One of the younger nurses was behind her, a girl with pink cheeks and eager eyes.

"Miss Nightingale, when we do disembark, I hope there won't be any more waiting around. I hope we can go right to our work of tending those poor fellows."

"The strongest of you," Florence said grimly, "will be wanted at the washtub." (They must realize, she added to herself, that no sentimentalism, no romantic nonsense would soften the work. It would be hard, bitterly hard.)

Another hour, and the English party was put ashore to walk the steep quarter-mile road to the hospital. Miss Nightingale went first, marching into the building's cen-

"The English nurse has come"

tral courtyard which was so gigantic that twelve thousand men had been known to drill there at one time. Just through the doorway, she stopped.

The courtyard held such filth as could not have been imagined, the rotting carcass of an army mule, piles of amputated human arms and legs flung out the windows onto the pavement, which ran with blood.

Florence stopped—and called to a soldier orderly.

"This debris must be hauled away and buried."

The orderly paused, detecting a tone of command.

"This courtyard must be cleaned, the pavement scrubbed. *Immediately!*"

"Y-yes, ma'am."

On a cot inside the entrance, Sir Alexander Montgomery Moore, a British officer, had been trying to sleep and forget his aching wounds. The voices in the courtyard had wakened him.

"I think," said Sir Alexander to his nearest neighbor, "that the English nurse has come."

The neighbor nodded a head swathed with dirty rags. "It's Miss Florence Nightingale. She has come."

11

A LADY WITH A LAMP

FLORENCE OPENED THE DOOR and stepped out upon the
upper gallery which stretched along three sides of the

She stepped out upon the upper gallery

building. She set down her lamp in the shelter of a pillar and pulled up the hood of her cape. The night was black, the sky mantled with low-hanging clouds pricked by an occasional star. The air was fresh and moist; she breathed it deeply and gratefully.

What a day this had been! Well, now it was behind her; there would be a meager interval to sleep—if she could. Then another day just as gruelling. She had no illusions about the days. She would have to take them as they came, one at a time, and do her best with them.

Neither had she illusions about the hospital. Rather, the two hospitals, for she had found that the General Hospital in Constantinople was also to be under her supervision. She must assign a few of her small nursing band to the General. She herself would stay here at the Barrack, keeping with her the more experienced women. Mrs. Drake was certainly a treasure, and Mrs. Roberts worth her weight in gold!

The Barrack, she knew now, after exploration, was simply that—a barrack, transformed to a hospital merely by the slapping on of a coat of whitewash. Its maximum capacity was 2,434 human beings and Balaclava had crowded it to the guards. Beneath these imposing yellow walls were cesspools and open sewers. The plumbing was woefully deficient—in fact, there was scarcely any plumbing at all, and no proper ventilation. The foulness of the interior atmosphere defied description—such a conglomeration of horrid smells! Rats and mice lived in the halls, vermin in the defective flooring. Yes, vermin crawled everywhere.

It was to this terrible place that soldiers, wounded in battle, were brought after a week-long voyage of neglect and suffering. Here they were unloaded, their garments stiff with drying gore, unloaded without ceremony, carried in and deposited, as if they had no more life in them than had that carcass of the army mule; most of them were laid on the bare floor because the few beds were occupied.

Wryly smiling, Florence remembered Sidney Herbert's vain hope that supplies would have arrived—and Dr. Andrew Smith's positive statement that nothing was wanting at Scutari.

Nothing? Florence could have made quite a memorandum of what was wanting. Hospital furniture, to start with, even the most ordinary and necessary pieces of furniture; beds, tables, chairs. After that, basins, buckets for water, soap, towels; and some candlesticks instead of the empty beer bottles now in use. Mattresses—oh, how she wished for mattresses! Mops, brooms, disinfectants, scrubbing brushes. "Scrub this courtyard," she had told the orderly. But there was not a scrubbing brush to be had anywhere. Not one. "I shall write to London for three hundred brushes," she thought. "It is not too many. Later I shall ask for more."

What about knives, forks, spoons, clean linen, hospital clothing? These men had no nightgowns. None at all. They lay in their dirty underwear and shirts, garments which were never washed. "Isn't clothing ever *laundered*?" she had demanded.

"Well," someone had said, "it is—at the rate of six shirts a month."

"You mean, six shirts a month for each man?"

"Oh, no, six shirts for *all* the men."

Hundreds, thousands of sick and dying men, and a monthly laundry of six shirts!

What about cotton, gauze, new bandages—bedpans?

Florence would have liked to present Dr. Smith with her memorandum of *essentials,* things needed now, just on the most cursory inspection, because you cannot manage a hospital without such things.

"Tomorrow," she said to herself, "I shall have the supplies I bought in Marseilles. How I wish I'd bought twice, ten times, as much! But, at least, tomorrow I shall have *some* supplies."

She thought back over the day, from the moment in which she had entered here. What had she done? First, there had been the parceling out of quarters, a vexing business because, though the Barrack was so large, it was now so full. One room, more spacious than the rest, was given to all the non-sectarian nurses as a dormitory; one medium-sized room was shared by the ten Roman Catholic nuns; the eight Anglican sisters had a somewhat smaller room. Something very small indeed, a cubbyhole, Florence had kept for herself and Mrs. Bracebridge. Charles Bracebridge and a young man who acted as Miss Nightingale's courier would sleep on divans in what was called the "sitting-room."

It did not really matter, Florence thought, if the members of her party were cramped and uncomfortable; they would be seldom in their rooms. But she was distressed for another reason. In the wards and the corridors, fever patients were thrown together with men who had not yet caught the fever.

"There should be separate areas for contagious cases. I shall rent a house somewhere nearby and move the fever patients into it."

This she would do with her own money. Silently she thanked Papa for the liberal allowance he had settled upon her; it would make possible many things which otherwise would have been impossible. Conceivably, her allowance from Papa might save many lives.

When the nurses had put down bags and boxes in their rooms, and changed into their uniforms and aprons, Miss Nightingale took them into the kitchen to prepare food for the sick men, some of whom were almost dead of starvation. The kitchen was equipped with huge kettles for boiling meat and vegetables; but no meat or vegetables were in the larder. There was very little foodstuff to cook that day. Well, a good store had been purchased in Marseilles and soon would be delivered from the harbour, and even now quantities of tea, rice, arrowroot, jellies for invalid diet were available—these Florence had brought in her luggage, never letting them get beyond reach.

After the patients were fed, the routine of wound-dressing began. Forty-five doctors comprised the medical staff, working in shifts, but the dressings to be done were unnumbered. Following after one of the surgeons, Florence herself attended to sixty-two patients, and then went from ward to ward, supervising, directing her subordinates. The surgeons were, as usual, amputating—not in a surgery or operating room; there was no such thing—but right out in the corridors, in plain view of everybody.

"I shall get a screen for this," Florence thought. "We must have a screen. The poor fellow who is to be operated on next is not helped by seeing his comrade die under the knife."

Soon, whenever she had an hour, she must write out some rules for the nurses. She intended that they must be strictly disciplined, for without discipline the best results could not be attained. The nurses must recognize and defer to her authority. She was their leader and she would be obeyed. But to enforce discipline, she would have to retain their affection and respect. They trusted her now; she must never do anything to lose their trust.

She hoped, too, to impress the doctors with her authority. Most of them she had liked in the first meeting. Most of them, she said to herself, were angels. A few were devils, heavy-handed men insensitive to the anguish of their patients. But all, she knew, were looking skeptically at Miss Nightingale, wondering what sort of person she was. It was an experiment, this admitting of women to a military hospital. She must convince them that it was a successful experiment.

There would be, she feared, some whom she could never convince, hidebound cynics, prejudiced medical men who would think of her as the rankest interloper and cry out against a government which would allow such absurdity—who might even be jealous of the Lady-in-Chief, which was the title Mr. Sidney Herbert had conferred upon her. But these reactionaries she must learn to ignore.

The night was darker now, every star obscured, rain was falling and the wind tugged at her skirts. She picked up the lamp and holding it before her, shielding the glow with her hand, she went through the door into the corridor, walking very softly and cautiously, making her way between the rows of huddled forms lying on the floor, seeing her shadow, tall and distorted, moving along the wall.

At the far end of the corridor, a young corporal, scarcely more than a boy, startled up from fitful napping and the incessant pain which had made him delirious. His eyes widened, and he lifted his battered body, propped himself on an elbow, staring incredulous.

"What—what's that?" he muttered hoarsely. "Why, it's a *lady!* A lady with a lamp!"

Then, strangely solaced, he slumped down again and slept.

12

CRIMEAN DAYS

THE BATTLE OF Inkerman occurred November 5, 1854.

In all the years which followed, the date would stand forth clearly in Florence Nightingale's memory because of what it had meant to her that year, at Scutari. Scarcely had she established the beginnings of some sort of routine, scarcely had she made a plan, when all was swept away with the influx of new patients.

There was but a half-hour's notice. "Get ready! More wounded are coming!" Then they were being borne in, five hundred and ten poor creatures, fallen before the Russian guns.

It was a time of frantic hurrying in the Barrack's corridors. Except for the Lady-in-Chief's poise, it would have been pandemonium. She refused to be dismayed. Did it seem that these men could not be accommodated? Well, they *must* be accommodated. Within eight hours, more than five hundred mattresses had somehow been pieced together, stuffed with straw, sewed up and placed on the floor; the men lying on the mattresses had been washed, their wounds had been dressed.

"A miracle!" said one of the nurses to Miss Nightingale. "We couldn't have done better in a London hospital."

Florence shrugged. "My opinion of London hospitals has never been high, but the worst of them is a garden of flowers compared to this."

Beneath an outward calm, she was worried, knowing that the voyage from the battle site, over unusually rough seas, had been a nightmare for the injured. The Turkish soldiers delegated as stretcher-bearers seemed needlessly callous and unfeeling—"the Turks, the very men for whom we are fighting!" Twenty-four of the wounded died during the day of their arrival. Dysentery, an implacable foe, had appeared in several of the wards.

Next day the surgeons performed hundreds of operations—for which no anesthetic was given. Though Sir John Hall, principal medical officer of the British Crimean forces, knew of this drug, its use was still in the experimental stages, and he did not favor it in cases of severe shock from gunshot wounds. Few men so disabled could survive the after-effects of chloroform, he said, and he would not risk losing patients in that way. Assisting the surgeons, Florence was astonished at the unshrinking heroism of the men. "It is really superhuman. We are steeped up to our necks in blood, yet they die or are cut up without a complaint!"

She wrote to a London acquaintance, "We have now *four miles* of beds, and not eighteen inches apart."

Yet at the end of that second day, she could reflect upon the good to be found even in the midst of appalling horrors. "I can truly say, like St. Peter, 'It is good for us to be here'—though I doubt whether if St. Peter had been here, he would have said so." Going her nightly rounds, she heard no groans, no murmurs of protest. Stoically, the men looked up at her, some of them smiled. "I was dreaming of my friends at home, ma'am." "I was dreaming of my mother."

The third day was a little bit easier and again Florence felt that she might eventually get the situation under control. But then the *Andes* made port with a ghastly freight.

The courier brought the word. "Five hundred and forty casualties. And two more ships loading at the Crimea."

Could they be housed in the Barrack? Yes, Florence said, there or in the General Hospital. "Let no soldier be told that we cannot take him in."

"But some Russian wounded are among the lot."

"We'll take in the Russians, too."

A dreadful pouring-in of shattered, mutilated men from the *Andes,* the other two vessels! Too many to be cared for, the doctors said; the more hopeful cases would have to be separated from those which seemed desperate. This weeding-out process was not to Miss Nightingale's liking. A life was a life; so long as a single breath animated a body, no effort should be spared.

"The five poor fellows lying in that corner, Sir John—can nothing be done for them?"

"Nothing, I fear."

"May I *try*?"

"Certainly. Try, if you will. It is futility."

She tried. Through the bleak hours between midnight and dawn, she worked over the five, feeding them with a spoon, bathing them, praying that they might gain a little strength. In the morning the surgeon examined them.

"They are in fair shape to be operated upon now."

"No longer hopeless cases?"

The surgeon shook his head. "I believe they may be saved."

There were additional troubles with which she must struggle. A tower room adjoining the nurses' quarters had been fitted up as an "extra diet kitchen," but daily the cook in charge reported that he had no foodstuffs beyond those Miss Nightingale herself had bought, which were almost depleted.

"Not a drop of milk, ma'am; and the bread is extremely moldy."

"Have we any butter?"

"None decent. What's here is mostly decomposed."

"Meat enough for broth?"

"Well, the meat is more like moist leather than like food. And we're waiting for potatoes; they're coming from France."

As the week passed, she knew what would be her two greatest obstacles. One was red tape; the other, a division of responsibility, the utter lack of co-ordination between departments. Conditions at Scutari were indeed scandalous, Mr. William H. Russell had portrayed them graphically; yet it would have been impossible to say who was at fault, whether committees or secretaries in London, or clerks and underlings in Constantinople. Perhaps the government as a whole was guilty. The result was all that concerned Florence Nightingale—and the result was chaos.

As Sidney Herbert had said, as many another cabinet member was declaring, supplies of all sorts had been sent in quantity to Constantinople, there was no excuse for such privations as the troops were suffering. But nobody knew whose liability these supplies were, nobody dared distribute them, since the duties of the various executors had never been defined. The casks and barrels and ton-weight containers at the Scutari wharf were enmeshed by the coils of red tape, forms, requisitions, regulations; the precious cargoes of supply ships were bound by sacred "service rules," which no one would question.

No one except Miss Nightingale. Asking for certain stores, she was told they had been received but could not be released to her—not without the procuring of endless signed papers. Such annoyances the Lady-in-Chief would tolerate only up to a point. She would run about from board to board, consulting this and that dignitary, complying with "service rules." But if too much put upon, she would (and frequently did) take the law into her own hands.

"I must have these stores. Why weren't they delivered to me?"

"Because the board hasn't inspected them, Miss Nightingale."

"Where is the board? No, don't answer. The board is not sitting just now. But my men are dying for want of these medicines, this lint. I must have them at once. Open the warehouse door."

"I can't, Miss Nightingale. I'd be court-martialed."

"No, I'll assume the blame. They can court-martial me. Open the door!"

Thus doors were opened to the grey-eyed, militant Lady-in-Chief.

The second obstacle was the attitude of some of the military officers. As she had foreseen, her presence here was resented by those who cherished tradition above the emergency's obvious need. "The Bird," they called her, these sulking adversaries; they laughed scornfully about the Bird and accused her of meddling. There was one ward at the Barrack in which the junior doctors were told by their superior to have nothing to do with Miss Nightingale, a very silly woman who insisted on getting things scrubbed (as if it mattered whether a hospital was clean!) and who "captured" the orderlies and coerced them to obey her.

"Open the warehouse door!"

Oh, yes, a thoroughly objectionable female, the Bird. Perhaps the most unpardonable, really maddening of her habits was that of always being right. You might dispute, argue with her, shout at her—and then circumstances would prove that she had facts, statistics at her finger-tips and had been right all along. Of course, such a woman must not be countenanced. Whisper about her, harass her—ridicule her!

Quite conscious of this opposition, Florence could afford to ignore it. The majority of the doctors were friendly. As for the infantry and cavalry officers with whom she had contact, she seemed able either to dominate or defy them. Only this morning there had been an incident in which she demonstrated her talent for quelling impudence.

She had been crossing the courtyard with a can of arrowroot in her arms—and what a wonderful treasure it was, unearthed from the depths of one of those locked warehouses!—when the young captain of cavalry rode up, halting his horse so suddenly that the animal reared and pawed the air.

"Where did you get that can?" the captain thundered. "Who granted you permission to go rifling the army stores?"

She had attempted no reply. Saying nothing at all, she had stared at him.

After a few minutes, his gaze had shifted; flushed and discomfited, he had ridden on.

But such things were of small consequence, weren't they? By contrast, she could meditate upon the courtesy of Lord Raglan, British commander of all troops in the Crimean area, who had officially welcomed Miss Nightingale and promised his support and sympathy. The Senior Chaplain at Scutari also was a stanch ally, tirelessly lending himself to any task she proposed, even writing a letter back to her father in praise of her. And there were the Bracebridges, sustaining her with their cheerfulness, working like Trojans wherever she posted them, constantly telling her—telling everyone—that the good she had done and was doing was priceless. And her nurses, the members of her little band, had an absolute faith in the decisions of the Lady-in-Chief.

And her patients? They were the ones who counted! "My children"—she thought of them as that. "My poor, dear children!" Well, no sane person could have doubted how her children felt about Miss Nightingale, how pathetically they depended upon her, how glad and grateful they were to find in this alien land an Englishwoman, somebody from home, who gently and mercifully tended them, whose only wish was to comfort and cure them.

"Yes," said Florence, "we are getting on nicely in many ways."

Meanwhile, the violent controversy about the misfortunes of the Crimean wounded continued to rage in the columns of the London *Times,* and several observers ventured out to see for themselves what was happening at Scutari.

Early among the visitors was the Reverend Sidney Godolphin Osborne, with letters of introduction from Mr. Sidney Herbert. By chance, perhaps, the Reverend Mr. Osborne was escorted around the Constantinople hospitals by one of the doctors who would not acknowledge the true state of affairs. Repeatedly Mr. Osborne asked if he might not contribute some financial help, either from his own or other funds.

"No, no," replied the doctor. "We have everything. Nothing is wanting."

The assertion did not deceive Mr. Osborne. He had eyes in his head and, moreover, a measure of familiarity with medical and surgical practices. He saw at a glance that, had not Miss Nightingale been there, disaster would have overwhelmed Scutari. Returning to England, he reported her efficiency and industry—not forgetting to mention also the jealousy which somewhat hindered her labors.

Then Mr. Macdonald, appointed to administer the *Times* fund, came to Scutari. Mr. Macdonald had by now a vast amount of money to expend for the relief of the wounded. His first call had been at the London War Office, where he was cordially received but assured that the government had made ample provision and it was scarcely likely any further relief was needed at the front. Nevertheless, Mr. Macdonald thought he might as well proceed to the Crimea, an idea in which Mr. Sidney Herbert heartily concurred. So Mr. Macdonald sailed for Constantinople.

Here he was met with the same smiling, polite rebuff. Everything was progressing beautifully in the hospitals; the patients lacked for nothing. Slightly puzzled, Mr. Macdonald was wondering whether to go back to London, when he encountered a surgeon of the 39th regiment.

"If you have money, sir," said the surgeon, "for pity's sake, get our troops warm winter clothing! Their only uniforms are the linen suits issued to them under the hot sun of Gibraltar. Bitter weather is at hand. The men will be literally frozen to death! After that, look into the Scutari hospitals where the Englishwomen are nursing."

Mr. Macdonald straightway went into the markets and bought blankets and woollen clothing for the men of the 39th regiment. Then he turned his steps toward Scutari.

The officers he spoke with there were just as polite as those in Constantinople. They were interested to know of the money collected by the *Times* from an aroused and patriotic public. Amazing, splendid that so much had been subscribed. But there was no occasion to spend even a fraction of it on provisions for the army hospitals.

"We are abundantly well off!"

The most august of all the officers had what seemed an inspiration. "Why doesn't the *Times* dispose of its fund by building an English church at Pera?"

His fellow officers applauded. "A fine idea! A worthy cause!"

But, somehow, the English church at Pera had scant appeal to Mr. Macdonald—and anyway, he had resolved to see his mission through. "I should like to talk to Miss Nightingale, please."

Oh, the Bird? Dubiously they took him to the Lady-in-Chief.

"Miss Nightingale, I have come out here to offer the financial aid of thousands of your admirers. But now I am told that no aid is needed. Our soldiers have everything."

Florence's face was a study. "You have seen the Barrack hospital, Mr. Macdonald?"

"No. Only some of its staff."

She got to her feet. "Come with me."

They went through the wards and she showed him what had been done—and what remained to be done; the narrow rooms, the narrower corridors packed with rows of crudely constructed cots, mattresses hastily thrown together, improvised beds; the hundreds of men who had been washed and clad in clean garments; the hundreds more who were still half-naked, their wounds padded with bloody rags. In and out, up and down, covering the four miles of a veritable City of Misery, he followed her slim, graceful figure, watching the eyes of the men light with new hope as she passed, hearing her greet this one and that, never raising her quiet voice yet instilling with a sentence something of her own tremendous courage.

"This is what we have, Mr. Macdonald," she said at last. "Is it everything?"

When he made his report on Scutari, Mr. Macdonald had all the facts, and the *Times* fund would be spent wisely to accomplish good. He could not refrain from giving his impression of Florence Nightingale herself. She was an "incomparable woman," a "ministering angel." "The popular instinct was not mistaken which, when she set out from England, hailed her as a heroine."

Another black night, and the Lady-in-Chief was starting, as was her custom, on the half-hour's walk from the Barrack to the General Hospital. She always went, she couldn't have slept without knowing that there, too, the nurses had done their best. The path was unpaved and treacherous and she had with her an invalid soldier, who carried a lantern in his hand—the one hand which was left him after the Battle of the Alma.

"Steady on, Miss Nightingale!" The soldier swung his lantern in a flickering arc. "It's all rocks here."

"Yes, they say that from this spot the most beautiful view in the world is visible—in the daytime, I mean."

"You haven't seen the view then, ma'am?"

"Oh, no. I am never out except like this, at night. I should probably be too busy even to look."

She laughed a little, with a faint note of gayety. Mr. Macdonald was a friend; he would not forget. Supplies were on the way.

13

PROBLEMS AND SOLUTIONS

"I ALWAYS THOUGHT I might end my days as matron of a hospital," said Florence. "I never in wildest fancy thought I should end them as purveyor to a large part of the British army."

It was a foggy winter morning ("Inkerman weather," the soldiers in the Barrack said) cold, cloudy, drizzling; the Lady-in-Chief sat at a pine table in the central room of the nurses' quarters. She had been writing to Mr. Sidney Herbert and had paused to chat with Mrs. Bracebridge who was rearranging the shelves with which the walls were lined.

"If you didn't act as purveyor, we should be in a muddle," said Selina. "Someone must act, and the real purveyor has lost himself in snarls of red tape."

"Yesterday I foraged in the stores. It's a cruise I make almost daily and not sanctioned—but the only way I know of to get first-hand evidence of our stock."

"What did you find, Flo?"

"Very little. The things unfound were more numerous. No mops, no plates, no wooden trays—though the engineer is having them made. No slippers, no shoebrushes or blacking, no scissors for cutting the men's hair, no chloride of zinc—which I especially wanted."

"A gloomy prospect, isn't it?"

"Yes," Florence said, "but there is a brighter side. A

great many things have somehow come under my juris-
diction, so that I can dole them out where needed." Smiling, she looked about the room, which was neatly stacked
with boxes, parcels, bundles of sheets and old linen, bolts
of flannel; tubs of butter, sugar, bread; kettles, sauce-
pans, books. "And here, Selina, is a notice that we're getting shirts, thousands of them, purchased with the *Times*
money—yes, and getting them by requisition from the
very official who a short while ago told Mr. Macdonald
that we had more shirts than we could use! Bless Mr.
Macdonald of the *Times!* And bless the Reverend Mr.
Osborne and all other messengers of good will!"

Selina nodded emphatically; and Florence turned
again to her letter, wrote a paragraph:

"I am a kind of general dealer in socks, shirts, knives
and forks, wooden spoons, tin baths, cabbage and car-
rots, operating tables, towels and soap, small tooth
combs, precipitate for destroying lice, bed pans and
stump pillows. I will send you a picture of my Caravanserai, into which beasts come in and out. Indeed the vermin might, if they had but 'unity of purpose,' carry off
the four miles of beds on their backs, and march with
them into the War Office."

At that moment, a nurse entered and stood respectfully
just inside the door. Florence put down her pen.

"Yes, Mrs. Drake?"

"Sago and beef tea for the fever cases in Ward Four,
if you please, Miss Nightingale."

"Very well. Mrs. Bracebridge has them on her shelves."

Selina handed the containers of sago and beef tea to
Mrs. Drake, who went out, her stiff skirts rustling.

"I suppose," Florence said, "the five big copper boilers
haven't been mended?"

"Not yet."

"So we have only eight good ones? Lucky that we opened our two extra diet kitchens and fixed the three supplementary boilers on the main stairway."

"You did it," Selina said. "Quite alone, too. No one else would have thought of it. But you saw it was taking three or four hours to serve each meal, with the nurses trudging interminable miles between the wards and the old kitchen, and the food getting chilled—and the weaker patients, those who couldn't feed themselves, often going hungry. You have simply revolutionized the cookery methods in the Barrack, Flo."

"And you have done as much with the laundry methods."

"No. You and I together, my dear."

The laundry had indeed been a problem. There were in Scutari more than two hundred soldiers' wives who had no shelter, no livelihood, who faced a winter of utter destitution. Florence had said something must be done for them; and the generous Bracebridges had promptly collected a sum of money for their care. Using this fund and donating money of her own, Florence had rented a house for the women to occupy; and then abruptly thinking of the hospital laundry, she had asked Selina why the soldiers' wives could not be hired to wash the hospital bedding. After only a slight delay, proper laundry equipment was installed in the rented house and the vast washing project begun. Now Selina had been deputized to manage it; and though conditions could not be described as ideal, they were certainly much improved.

Florence finished and sealed her letter to Mr. Herbert. She would have had to stop writing anyway, because a group of orderlies waited at the door with requests or inquiries, and she knew that the customary rush of business had started. The nurses called this room the Tower of Babel; by late morning and then all through the rest of the day, it was besieged by people—by the nurses themselves, nuns, Turkish and Greek servants, French and Italian servants, British officers and surgeons. Everybody wanted to see and talk with Miss Nightingale; everybody was intent on his particular assignment, each spoke his own language. Sometimes also the Lady-in-Chief would hold here the "councils" over which she presided with firmness and dignity; and this was her office (at least, the only one she had) from which she had sent frequent reports to the government and to benefactors and supporters in England.

Many of the consultations were of the most serious import. Some were trivial—

"Good morning, Mrs. Lawfield. What can I do for you?"

"Miss Nightingale, excuse me, ma'am. I came out, as you know, prepared to submit to everything, to be put upon in every way. But there are some things, ma'am, one can't submit to."

"What things, for example?"

"There is the caps, ma'am, that suit one face and won't suit another." Mrs. Lawfield twisted a corner of her apron and looked very unhappy. "If I'd known, ma'am, about the caps, great as was my desire to come out to nurse at Scutari, I wouldn't have come, ma'am."

The Lady-in-Chief thought a moment. The costume she had devised for the Nightingale nurses was a gray tweed wrapper-like gown, a worsted jacket and, for outdoor wear, a short woollen coat and a brown holland scarf embroidered in red with the words "Scutari Hospital." The close-fitting cap was intended to give the wearer a sober, modest appearance; Miss Nightingale had not been bothered at all as to whether it was becoming.

How foolish of Mrs. Lawfield to bother! But she was such a good nurse—perhaps an exception should be made.

"I daresay you may go without the cap, Mrs. Lawfield."

"Oh, thank you, ma'am."

Completely satisfied, Mrs. Lawfield bowed and withdrew.

Also interrupting the stream of significant callers at the Caravanserai was Thomas. Twelve years old, a drummer boy, the pride of his regiment, the pet of the hospital, Thomas had fallen quite in love with Miss Nightingale. "I'm her man," he said, and had announced that he was ready to die for her—or, when the war was over, to forsake his drum and his military career, to go back to England with her.

"Well, Thomas?"

He saluted. "I just dropped in, Miss Nightingale, to tell you what my comrades are saying about you."

"What is that?"

"Before you came, they say, there was such cussin' and swearin' as you never heard; but since you came, it's all as holy as a church. You're the Angel of the Crimea, they say, and bad men can't be bad in the presence of an angel."

"Thank you, Thomas. I shall remember. But you had best run along now."

"Yes, ma'm," said Thomas.

The rush continued, all the many people who must bring their troubles and perplexities to Miss Nightingale and ask for remedy. Gradually they had realized that this was the one person they could rely upon; gradually, by steady pressure, she had established her authority here. She had done so by never sparing herself, never for an instant saying, even to herself, that she would not succeed. By what she knew to be superhuman effort she was accomplishing a work of reformation which to the world must have seemed impossible. But to her, failure had been the impossible thing; and she had always known she could not fail.

She liked to think that in all these weeks she had not allowed herself an hour's recreation, had denied herself proper rest and sleep and fresh air, that often mealtimes were passed over and forgotten while she toiled. To have given less than every ounce of strength would not have been enough—would not have been what God expected of her. For God was the only master she would acknowledge; she was His representative at Scutari; the work she did was His work. In that thought was all the reward, all the pleasure she desired.

" 'Thy will be done'—"

In the evening, she revised again her disciplinary rules for the nurses. It was probably inevitable that, human nature being as it is, she should have been disappointed in some of the selections made back there, so quickly, in London. One young girl had been sent home almost immediately upon arrival; she was unqualified professionally, unfit morally. Much to the Lady-in-Chief's joy, her place had been taken at once by a Kaiserswerth nurse from Constantinople. Soon afterward, four more nurses were dismissed; they would not accept Miss Nightingale's rigid code and so she had felt she could not keep them on. A half-dozen she had transferred from the Barrack to the General Hospital. Now that she knew them well, she could estimate that of the original thirty-eight, only sixteen were really efficient at their job; but of these sixteen, five or six deserved (like Mrs. Lawfield) a rating of excellent.

Writing by lamplight in the Caravanserai, Florence outlined her ideas of nursing, of ward management. Every nurse, she wrote, should have undergone a course of training and should be, upon completing the course, subject to the direction of a female superintendent. The nurse must never think of herself as a rival of the doctor's, but must be wholly subordinate to the doctor, doing his bidding, heeding his instructions, never prescribing for a patient, never waiting upon a patient, except as the doctor specified. But nurses must not be regarded, by either doctors or persons outside the profession, as domestic servants—as housemaids; for they were never meant to be that, and theirs was a higher calling. A nurse's trained skill, her precious time, must not be wasted on such chores as the most unskilled slavey could as capably perform. The employment therefore of domestic servants and orderlies in a hospital must not be done away with.

Nurses must seek to exert a moral influence; they must always appear in the regulation uniform with the badge, must not trim their "bonnet-caps" with flowers or ribbons, must not have more than a small and designated amount of spirituous liquor to drink, could walk out only by permission, and then with their superintendent or in parties of three.

Though she didn't know it, Miss Nightingale was putting down the fundamental rules which, somewhat altered, would govern the nursing in military hospitals for generations to come.

"Flo! The post is here—and a letter for you!"

Florence looked up at Selina Bracebridge who had pushed aside the burlap curtain hanging in the doorway of the Caravanserai.

"A letter?"

"Forwarded by Mr. Herbert. It is dated 'Windsor Castle, December 6, 1854.'"

"Windsor Castle? From the Queen, Selina?"

Yes, from the Queen. Florence read it aloud:

"'Would you tell Mrs. Herbert that I beg she would let me see frequently the accounts she receives from Miss Nightingale or Mrs. Bracebridge, as *I hear no details of the wounded*, though I see so many from officers, etc., about the battlefield, and naturally the former must interest *me* more than anyone.

"'Let Mrs. Herbert also know that I wish Miss Nightingale and the ladies would tell these poor, noble wounded and sick men, that *no one* takes a warmer interest or feels *more* for their sufferings or admires their courage and heroism *more* than their Queen. Day and night she thinks of her beloved troops. So does the Prince.

"'Beg Mrs. Herbert to communicate these my words to those ladies, as I know that *our* sympathy is much valued by these noble fellows.—Victoria.'"

There was a little silence; then Selina said, rather tearfully, "God save the Queen!"

"I shall ask the Senior Chaplain to go from ward to

ward, reading the letter," Florence said. "Even the dying will want to know of Her Majesty's loving kindness."

When Selina had gone off in search of the Senior

It was mostly hushed

Chaplain, Florence took up her lamp to make her final round of the Barrack.

The place was pitchy black tonight; in some rooms, beneath a vaulted roof, like an eerie cavern; in the low-ceiled corridors, like a tunnel burrowing underground. It was mostly hushed, only an occasional stifled moan disturbing the silence; no other movement than an occasional figure tossing on a lumpy mattress, or unyielding cot, an orderly nodding in a chair, a nurse slipping softly by on noiseless feet. The cold wind buffeted at the windows and, far away, could be heard the dull roar of waves on the Straits of the Dardanelles—"like the sound of the Derwent," Florence thought, "when Parthe and I listened to it in our nursery at Lea Hurst, with the dolls!"

Through all the rooms she went, shifting a pillow here, straightening a blanket there, her shadow silhouetted in the ring of yellow which bobbed along the wall.

"The lady with the lamp!" It was a murmur running swiftly before the advancing ray of light; and men reached out to touch the shadow on the wall; and those who could, leaned forward to kiss the shadow as she passed.

14

SCUTARI WINTER

THE WINTER WAS hard and long in the Crimea. The British and French troops were entrenched around the Russian stronghold of Sevastopol; but sleet, snow and mud kept all armies at a standstill and the only military operations were a few siege skirmishes which could not be marked up as victories or defeats for either side. During those months disease was the principal foe of the British soldier, and disease had its many triumphs. Poorly fed and equipped, exposed to severe weather, the men by hundreds were sick with coughs, fever, pneumonia, dysentery.

Between the peninsular ports and Scutari, ships plied constantly, bringing more and more patients to Miss Nightingale's hospitals. Such arrivals Florence could cope with calmly enough—they were all in the day's work; but one ship which docked brought passengers of another sort, whose coming angered and disconcerted the Lady-in-Chief.

She was seated that day in the tower room at her table; she wore her usual costume, a black merino frock trimmed with black velvet, white linen collar, cuffs, apron and cap. She heard footsteps in the corridor, the curtain in the doorway was lifted. She glanced up—and saw her old friend, Miss Mary Stanley. Behind Miss

Stanley was a sizable group of feminine figures, dozens it seemed, dressed for traveling, luggage in their hands.

"Are you surprised, Florence?" said Miss Stanley.

"We've come to help you with the nursing"

"There are forty of us; we've come to help you with the nursing."

Florence got up. No, she was not surprised; she had been forewarned. But she was irate. Miss Stanley was a daughter of the Bishop of Norwich, she was a nurse of some experience and Florence had known her intimately for years. But Florence had not (and this was the point!) invited Miss Stanley to help at Scutari.

"You are here by Mr. Sidney Herbert's authority," Florence said coldly. "He sent you, after Mr. Bracebridge and the Reverend Mr. Osborne told him we were badly off and understaffed. But, of course, Mr. Herbert has no authority, and the gentlemen misinformed him. We are not badly off, we do not need more nurses. In fact, we are so crowded that we can't find quarters for you." She hesitated. "You may sleep here tonight, Mary; perhaps there will be a place for your party in the General Hospital. Later you can all be assigned to other hospitals in Constantinople, or somewhere."

When, rather abashed, Miss Stanley and her companions had withdrawn, Florence wrote furiously to Sidney Herbert. Yes, she had received his letter which said that Mary Stanley was leaving for Scutari. And now Miss Stanley had come. Meddling *women*? Well, what about meddling *men*? How dared anyone go over the head of the Lady-in-Chief to plan improvements at Scutari? Mr. Herbert must understand once and for all that, much as she liked him, Miss Nightingale would stand for no interference from him—or from any source. She had agreed to assume full management here; that she would assume and nothing less.

Her pen scratched over the paper. "You have sacrificed the cause so near my heart, you have sacrificed me, a matter of small importance now; you have sacrificed your own written word to a popular cry." Perhaps Mr. Herbert thought that, having found shelter for these forty poor wanderers, Miss Nightingale ought to resign?

She recalled to him how she had worked to gain the confidence of the medical officers; how by incessant vigilance, day and night, she had drilled her little band until now routine reigned where wildest upheaval had been before. Forty more nurses? To have women scampering about the wards of a Military Hospital all day long, which they would do were their numbers so increased would relax the discipline and increase their leisure. It would be both improper and absurd.

Yes, Miss Nightingale was thinking seriously of resigning!

Mr. Herbert wilted under this blast and was all apologies. People in England were enthusiastic and sentimental, he said, and probably had no idea of what the task at Scutari had been. He had acted impulsively; and at the behest, too, of Mr. Osborne, Mr. Bracebridge and other well-intentioned persons. But Florence must feel free to do just as she saw best. Miss Stanley and her whole party could be returned to England at Mr. Herbert's expense, and the incident closed.

Mrs. Herbert wrote to Mrs. Bracebridge, "I am heartbroken about the nurses, but I do assure you, if you send them all home without a trial, you will lose some really valuable women."

By the time these letters came, Florence had simmered down considerably and was thinking that a few recruits to her staff might be a boon. She reorganized the Barrack nurses, increasing the roster to fifty. Miss Stanley and the rest then went to hospitals at Koulali and Balaclava.

But between Miss Nightingale and Miss Stanley there was a definite estrangement and, parting at Scutari, they did not meet again. Florence had no regrets. Not this bond of friendship or any other could weigh in the balance with what she believed to be her duty. Individuals meant nothing—her cause everything!

With the men in the wards, her "children," Miss Nightingale was always infinitely compassionate and tender; but it was not in her character to take petty persecution without striking back, and more than once that winter she lashed out at her critics. In letters home she loosed her remarkable talent for sarcasm, writing mockingly of those physicians and military officials who still were not her friends, giving them satirical nicknames, pillorying them with single sentences of scorn.

The nurses, too, sometimes earned her wrath.

One day three of her staff appeared before her and announced that they were going to get married. So, in spite of the Lady-in-Chief's watchfulness, romance had flowered in the gloomy Barrack? She was incensed. Marriage was all very well in its place—which was not at Scutari. Some women must marry, perhaps. But not nurses! Why could they not see, these three stupid creatures, that only in serving God was their real hope for earthly happiness?

But the nurses went on and got married, just the same —as she had supposed they would. In such circumstances, her hands were tied, her superior insight of no avail; she could do nothing to prevent their folly.

She concerned herself with her patients and the condition of the Crimean army as a whole. It was pitiable, and showed all too plainly that something, somewhere, was very much amiss. The exhaustion of the ailing men unloaded at Scutari was evidence of gross error on somebody's part. Frost-bitten, thinly clad, half-starved, gaunt and hollow-eyed, they had been an easy prey to illness and were slow to recover. When discharged from the hospitals, these men would go back to their former wretched environment—and would probably soon be in hospitals again.

But even though the government's machinery for relief seemed to have bogged down, there still were private means of providing for the soldiers. Money in large sums had been sent to Miss Nightingale, from England, from Australia, New South Wales and New Zealand—thousands of pounds. If the dilemma was one of nobody's knowing that things were wrong, or nobody's caring sufficiently to straighten out the sad state of affairs, then Florence, who knew so well and cared with all her heart, was ready to step into the breach.

She urged Mr. Herbert to buy and ship immediately warm clothing for the Crimean troops; and she presented to him an incisive suggestion by which the meshes of red tape could be cut and supplies, including food, quickly transported to the front. Warehouses must be built, she said, and porters hired. In March, 1855, this suggestion was adopted and a road paved in the Crimea, so that freight thereafter was delivered to its destination without the old postponements and endless delays.

She said also that the hospital orderly system and the ambulance corps must be reorganized. She showed with statistics the faultiness of the army's purveying department, and how it could be made effectual. As for the military kitchen management and cookery, she contemptuously denounced it.

The army hospital's way of preparing a meal was to issue each man his day's rations, to wrap these rations in separate small bags of coarse cloth—and then to fling all the bags, hundreds of them, into huge boiling cauldrons. Of course, all the food which came out of the cauldron tasted alike, and none was fit to eat, especially in invalid cases where a delicate diet was essential. Miss Nightingale's extra diet kitchens corrected this difficulty at the Barrack and General Hospitals; and she demanded that her method be instituted elsewhere.

Some of these changes were made at once; many more were to be of benefit in the future.

Once during the winter, Miss Nightingale herself became a builder; it was a venture which earned her much criticism in hostile camps and just as much praise in others. Several wards in the Barrack were simply too dilapidated for further use, eight hundred beds were in these rooms from which all patients must be removed. Lord Raglan had told Miss Nightingale that many more patients might be expected soon, but not he—or anyone —would be responsible for ordering repairs.

This was a predicament calling for extreme measures. Florence engaged two hundred workmen and had the repairs made, paying the bill out of her own pocket. Somewhat later the War Department approved her action and reimbursed her.

Meanwhile in England, Lord Palmerston had been called to head the government as Prime Minister, and there were many cabinet changes. The offices of Secretary of State and Secretary at War were combined under Lord Panmure. Mr. Sidney Herbert was for a while Secretary for the Colonies, and then resigned, though he had not lost interest in the Crimean soldiers' plight or in Florence Nightingale's work. The new government appointed Lord Shaftesbury to investigate sanitation problems in the Scutari hospitals, and a commission was sent out for that purpose.

Lord Shaftesbury had a reputation as a humanitarian,

in his political career he had toiled always for the betterment of the laboring classes. Florence Nightingale had
become acquainted with him when she taught in the
Ragged Schools of London and Lord Shaftesbury was
president of the Ragged Schools Union, a position he
held for forty years. It was only natural, perhaps, that
these two believers in reform should have identical views
on the need for drastic reform of Scutari's sanitation
facilities. When the commissioners had surveyed the Barrack, and thought about the death rate which rose ap-
pallingly in the winter months, the building of new
sewers, flooring and walls was recommended—the very
thing which Miss Nightingale had been urging for ever
so long, and to which previous officials had turned a deaf
ear.

Indeed, the commission worked swiftly and compe-
tently; Florence told Lord Shaftesbury it had "saved the
army." One of its members, Dr. John Sutherland, was a
friend with whom the Lady-in-Chief was to have a close
future association.

Florence wrote to Parthe, "We have established a
reading room for convalescents, which is well attended.
The men are so glad to read. The officers look on with
composure and say to me, 'You are spoiling the brutes.' "

The Barrack Hospital reading room was set up to provide leisure occupation for hours which, Florence knew,
might otherwise be spent in drinking; and despite the
skeptical smiles of the officers, she went on with it. Soon
drunkenness among the soldiers was the exceptional
rather than the usual thing. The officers said they could
not account for this; a phenomenon, they said; and surely
Miss Nightingale's reading room had nothing to do with

it. The Bird was heard to say that she regretted having no trained teacher to start a course of study. Lessons for the soldiers? "Impossible!" exclaimed the officers.

Well, she would see about that.

As another experiment, she talked to the men on the subject of sending their pay home to their families. She had written this idea to the Queen, who transmitted her letter to the cabinet—where it was discussed. Some of the statesmen were for it; more were against it. The majority opinion seemed to be that "the soldier is not a remitting animal."

"Miss Nightingale," asserted one of the secretaries, "knows nothing of the British soldier."

She did not wait for the cabinet's sanction, but proceeded to create a Money Order Office, in which on four afternoons a month she received the money any soldier wished to forward to his home. Mr. Sam Smith was the receiving agent in England, passing on these allowances to the mothers, wives and children of the various soldiers. About £1,000 was taken in each month, and dispatched overseas. The idea spread, money order offices were opened in Constantinople, in Scutari, Balaclava and at the army headquarters in the Crimea. Within six months' times £71,000 was sent home. "All of it," Florence said, "money rescued from the canteen."

She tried in yet another way to rescue the soldier's pay from the canteen—by setting up the "Inkerman Café" on the Bosporus shore. She made the coffee house attractive and comfortable, and decorated it with a picture of the Queen, which Victoria had sent from Windsor Castle.

Encouraged by the popularity of the Inkerman Café, and convinced that she was not really "spoiling the brutes," she established classrooms in the Barrack, equipped them with books, games, music, maps, a magic lantern and stereoscope. When this project became known, everybody in England wished to contribute. The Queen and the Duchess of Kent made liberal donations; the government, through Sir Henry Storks, bought and equipped a second school building outside the Barrack —and two schoolmasters came from London to conduct the classes.

Florence's own faith in her "children" grew by leaps and bounds. "I have never seen so teachable and helpful a class as the Army generally. Give them opportunity promptly and securely to send money home, and they will use it. Give them schools and lectures and they will come to them. Give them books and games and amusements and they will leave off drinking. Give them suffering and they will bear it. Give them work and they will do it."

How did the men feel about Miss Nightingale? Listen to them as they talk together in the wards:

"Wonderful, she is, at cheering up anyone who's a bit low!"

"She's all full of life and fun when she speaks to us."

"If she were commanding our troops, we'd be in Sevastopol in a week!"

"Yes, and if the Queen should die, they ought to make Miss Nightingale the queen. 'Queen Florence!' How is it, mates?"

"Aye, aye! Queen Florence!"

A visitor from England in January, 1855, wrote that to see Florence in the Barrack made intelligible to him the saints of the Middle Ages. "If the soldiers were told that the roof had opened, and she had gone up palpably to Heaven, they would not be the least surprised. They quite believe she is in several places at once."

But in England, now and again, someone wondered if maybe Miss Nightingale was too broad-minded about religion. Was it so that she had no Presbyterian nurses at Scutari? A curious oversight! Hadn't she been quoted as saying that some of the Catholic nuns were the truest Christians she had ever met? Hadn't she written of the Reverend Mother Moore as her mainstay, "devoted, heart and head, to serve God and mankind?"

Was this Popery? Well, we must write to the London *Times!*

Echoes reached Florence. "They tell me," she commented in a letter to Mr. Herbert, "that there is a religious war about poor me in the *Times*, and that Mrs. Herbert has generously defended me. I do not know what I have done to be so dragged before the Public. But I am so glad that my God is not the God of the High Church, or of the low, that He is not a Romanist or an Anglican—or a Unitarian. I don't believe He is even a Russian, though His events go strangely against us. (N. B.—A Greek once said to me at Salamis, 'I do believe God Almighty is an Englishman.'")

The fact was that she made no distinctions on religious grounds between her nurses; and Miss Shaw Stewart, Mrs. Roberts and Mrs. Drake, Protestants all, were as much her favorites as were the nuns. She based her judgment solely on ability—and intolerance she had always detested.

It was spring at last and the number of cases at the Barrack so reduced that Florence decided to cross the

Black Sea to inspect the Balaclava hospitals. The trip might refresh her, for far from feeling satisfied with what she had done, she was haunted by the thought of what more she might have done.

She took with her a few companions; Mr. Bracebridge, Mrs. Roberts, two cooks, a courier, an invalided soldier and Thomas, the drummer boy.

May 5, she wrote home: "Poor old Flo steaming up the Bosporus in the *Robert Lowe* or *Robert Slow* (for an exceedingly slow boat she is) taking back 420 of her patients, a draught of convalescents returning to their regiments to be shot at again. What suggestions do the above ideas make to you in the Embley drawing-room? Stranger ones perhaps than to me, who, having been at Scutari six months today, am in sympathy with God, fulfilling the purpose I came into the world for."

15

"THE DAUGHTER OF ENGLAND!"

FROM THE DECK of the *Robert Lowe*, Florence saw the
several large ships, the many small boats anchored in the

There were large ships anchored in the harbour of Balaclava

harbour of Balaclava. The shore and the landing pier were dark with people.

"Who are they all? Why have they gathered here?" she asked Charles Bracebridge.

In a moment she had her answer. These were friends, people who had heard of Miss Nightingale and her splendid work, who hoped now for a glimpse of Scutari's Lady-in-Chief. No sooner had her vessel steamed in than the welcome began, doctors and officials of Balaclava boarded the *Robert Lowe* to offer their respects and compliments. For more than an hour, Florence greeted her guests—and she was rather bored about it; she disliked such functions anyway; and what she really wanted was to go ashore and inspect hospitals. Lord Raglan, she was told, was scheduled to arrive shortly.

"I am sorry I cannot wait for him," Florence said, "but my errand is not of a social nature and I have no time to waste."

Thus, she missed the coming of the British commander. She went directly from the waterfront to the biggest of the hospitals where she started her tour of inspection.

But she did not wish to seem discourteous, and next day she set out on horseback with an escort to visit Lord Raglan at his headquarters in the camp of the besieging army.

The mare she rode was a beautiful creature, so light brown in color as to look golden in the sunshine, and so spirited that only an expert horsewoman could have kept in the saddle, as the party pushed forward along muddy paths which were noisy and crowded with refugees. This was spring, fine warm weather and the thousands of Crimean inhabitants made homeless by the war were on the move again after a winter of hardship and despair, streaming back toward the farms from which military maneuvers had driven them. Everywhere was tumult— straggling lines of oxen, sheep, cattle and mules, with their owners plodding behind; strings of carts and wagons, pulled by donkeys or by hand, laden with household goods, with grain sacks and crude farm implements. In the ditches beside the paths were overturned and abandoned conveyances, wreckage, rusty cannon left by retreating troops.

A scene of bedlam. But Florence rode without accident through it, though the golden mare often shied and reared and pranced skittishly.

"You are not afraid, Miss Nightingale?" queried an officer in her escort.

"Afraid?" She smiled. "I've ridden since I was a little girl." She thought for a minute of that little girl she had been, racing madly over the English downs, jumping fences—with Parthe as companion, or the Reverend Mr. Giffard or some other of those dear friends at home.

They went first to the village of Kadikoi, stopping to see the hospital there. Then they climbed to the top of a nearby hill which overlooked the approaches of Sevastopol. Alighting, they stood on the crest and Florence gazed down at the white tents which by thousands flanked the city walls. Puffs of white smoke billowed intermittently skyward, cannon boomed and muskets crackled fire. Sevastopol was beleaguered, was grimly resisting, but surrender was predicted.

Thomas scrambled over the rocks to stand beside Miss Nightingale. "The Russians can't last much longer," he said, his eyes bright with interest. "A wonderful sight, isn't it, ma'am?"

She shook her head sadly and turned away, knowing what the sight meant in human anguish, praying in her heart for the end of all fighting.

On the outskirts of the British lines was a hospital which she wished to inspect. Word of her visit had preceded her; as she went through the wards, the men received her with rejoicing. Lord Raglan was not there or in his headquarters. Unaware of Miss Nightingale's coming, he had gone off early to a distant area of the camp.

"But that doesn't matter," Florence said. She had now called upon him and exchanged courtesies—and she would have more time to spend with the sick and wounded.

Emerging an hour later, she was delighted to find a group of old acquaintances outside the hospital. These were former patients of hers at Scutari, men sent back from the Barrack to active duty, rallying around her now to shout their greetings.

"Miss Nightingale! Hurrah for the Lady-in-Chief!"

It was almost too much for the golden mare, who pranced and capered like a circus pony. But Florence's grip on the reins was steady, as she bowed and smiled.

A mile farther on, one of the escort officers said that they had best circle back toward safer terrain.

"Oh, no!" protested Florence. "Let us go up ahead."

"But the guns are firing, Miss Nightingale."

"I want a view of Sevastopol," she said, and while he hesitated, she pulled aside and trotted toward the city walls, and was at a point where the gates could be seen.

But here a sentry darted from ambush, waving his arms.

"Sharp firing! Turn away!"

"I am Florence Nightingale—"

"Just so!" cried the sentry. "The Russians would be glad to aim at you, ma'am."

She laughed. "Please let me go on. I'm not in the least afraid."

"No!" said the sentry, but then his arms dropped, for the lady was going on, unheeding. "Ah, well, if you must—"

"Miss Nightingale," said the escort officer, "I beg you to dismount and take refuge in that stone redoubt over there!"

Florence dismounted. The view from the redoubt was good, but still she was not contented. "I am going into the trenches."

The sentry was horrified. "The trenches? You will be killed!"

"Oh, I don't think so."

"Madam," said the sentry, "if anything happens, these gentlemen will witness that I did not fail to warn you of the danger."

She had been peering through a telescope; lowering it, she tied her cap strings, gathered her cape about her and smiled at him. "My good young man," she said, "more dead and wounded have passed through my hands than I hope you will ever see in the battlefield during the whole of your military service. Believe me, I am not afraid."

So she went into the trenches, walked through those deep and narrow gashes in the earth, stepped upon the ramparts, touched the gun carriages and the iron muzzles of the mortar cannon. Lastly she climbed up and sat a moment upon the center mortar.

One of her party, a Frenchman with an instinct for

the dramatic, cried out: "Behold the heroic daughter of England—the soldier's frend!"

A mighty burst of cheering rose from the trenches. "Bravo! Long live the daughter of England!"

"Henceforth this mortar shall be known as the 'Nightingale mortar!'" cried the Frenchman.

"Bravo!"

Now all the regiment had seen the valiant lady on the mortar, everyone was shouting: "It's Florence Nightingale! The Angel of the Crimea!"

The noise was so great that even the Russians inside the walls of Sevastopol heard and were startled. Florence herself was startled. Her face flushed with emotion, tears in her eyes, she got down from her perilous lookout.

"Miss Nightingale, we must go back to Balaclava—"

"Yes," she said quietly. "I am ready."

She was very tired that night—from the excitement and the long, rough ride, she thought. But in the morning, she was up and in the saddle for a trip to some convalescent huts located on the mountain slope, eight hundred feet above sea level. The sun was hot, with a brassy glare. All day the sun beat upon her and with evening a damp wind blew. She was quite exhausted; but next day she made the trip again, taking nurses who were much needed in the huts. For three days more she continued with her work of supervising the outlying infirmaries and convalescent posts—and then she could not continue.

She was ill. She had been stricken with that worst of scourges, Crimean fever.

The doctors in attendance were worried and ordered

that she be cared for in the mountainside sanatorium, where the pure air might speed recovery. They placed her on a stretcher and six soldiers, men whom she once had nursed, who knew and loved her, carried the stretcher through the streets of Balaclava and up the mountain road. Mrs. Roberts walked beside her, holding a white umbrella to shield Miss Nightingale from the pitiless sun; Thomas, weeping like a baby, marched behind and following Thomas was a doleful procession of mourning soldiers.

"Florence Nightingale is ill! She is near death!"

The tidings spread through Balaclava, echoed in Scutari. The patients in her own hospitals heard and buried their faces in their pillows, grieved and sobbing. The tidings were wafted to England, over the new electric cable recently completed. In London the message created consternation. Miss Nightingale ill? Dying, perhaps? This was a national calamity!

At five o'clock in the afternoon of a crucial day, two horsemen galloped to the door of the sanatorium and knocked. It was raining; their guttapercha cloaks were dripping wet, their hats sodden.

"We've come to inquire for Miss Nightingale," said one of them, to Mrs. Roberts who had opened the door.

"Hist! Don't speak so loud, my man!" Mrs. Roberts gestured for silence.

"Is Miss Nightingale here?"

"Yes, she is, poor lady—"

The visitor strode in, but Mrs. Roberts planted herself in the way. "No, you don't!"

"I must see Miss Nightingale."

"Oh, must you? And who are you?"

"Only a soldier, madam, but I've traveled long miles. My name is Raglan. Miss Nightingale knows me."

"Raglan?" Mrs. Roberts paused—and just then Florence called from her sickroom.

"It's Lord Raglan, Mrs. Roberts. Tell him I have a very bad fever, he must not see me."

Without more ado, Lord Raglan pushed by the nurse, went into the room and seated himself on a stool at the bedside. "I, too, am without fear," he said, "of fever or anything else, Miss Nightingale. I felt that I should never rest until I had expressed to you my thanks for all you've done and my wish that you may soon be well again." He stared at her, noticing how thin she was, her lips parched, her cheeks stained with unhealthy color. Was this to be her fate? Florence Nightingale, dying like this, her task unfinished? No, Lord Raglan did not think so. She would be spared. He got up. "Good-bye, Miss Nightingale. You will recover."

For twelve days more her condition was serious, but now the fever was receding, she was gaining a little strength. The doctors said that in a week she could be sent home to England.

"I am going home," she said, "to *Scutari*."

There was no arguing with the Lady-in-Chief. If she said she was going to Scutari, that was what she would do. The doctors sighed and summoned the stretcher-bearers. Down the mountain she was carried, and so to the port. At least, though, she could sail more comfortably than in a troop ship; Lord Ward's private yacht was in the Balaclava harbor and Selina Bracebridge, who had come in haste at the first news of Florence's illness, arranged for the use of this lighter, faster craft.

In June, only a little more than a month from the time

of her embarking for the Crimea, Florence saw again the lovely spires and minarets of Constantinople's skyline.

"I shall get well rapidly here," she said to Mrs. Bracebridge. "I am so happy to be back with my people."

Her people! All the men in the wards at the Barrack and the General Hospital wept their thankfulness and spoke her name with reverent awe. She had returned, their Angel—more slender and delicate than ever in figure, her hair cut short, with just the curling ends showing beneath her linen cap, her hands white and fragile—but walking with the same firm tread, smiling with the same tenderness, toiling with the same unflagging zeal for the welfare of her "children."

If one thing had been needed to intensify her popularity in England, this illness and recovery had been the thing. Florence Nightingale was now the most talked-of, the most famous woman in the world, a public idol, the object of universal admiration and acclaim. Songs with such titles as *The Woman's Smile, The Soldier's Cheer, The Shadow on the Pillow* appeared and were sold by the thousands of copies in music shops. Poems and artists' sketches of the Lady with the Lamp were printed, with both short and long biographies, in all the papers, from the smallest country journal to the publications of the great universities. Stationers brought out note-paper with her portrait as a watermark, or with a lithographed view of Lea Hurst; and there were scores of different pictures of her run off and sold by hawkers in the streets. China figurines in her likeness were on the counters of every shop, and tradesmen adorned their paper bags with sentimental pictures portraying her as she ministered to the wounded. Life boats, emigrant ships, streets, waltzes, puddings, articles of wearing apparel were named in her honor; and at fairs throughout the country and at seaside resorts were wax exhibits, sometimes life-size, depicting her at her merciful work. Race horses were named for her—"The Forest Plate handicap was won by Miss Nightingale, beating Barbarity and nine others"—and dozens, hundreds, of new babies were christened "Florence." Indeed, that magic name swept through the British Isles and the Empire, and so on around the globe, guaranteeing that a whole generation of Florences would grow up to keep green the memory of this first and noble Florence.

Lea Hurst and Embley became famous in her reflection, with gifts of every description pouring in (to be sorted and acknowledged by Parthe) and people driving or tramping out on Sundays to see the places where their heroine had lived. When it became known that Miss Nightingale did not intend to come home to recuperate but had said, "I will stand out the war with any man!", all these evidences of adoration were redoubled.

It boiled up at last in a huge public meeting held in London, the purpose of which was "to give expression to a general feeling that the services of Miss Nightingale in the hospitals of the East demand the grateful recognition of the British people." The *Times* said there never had been assembled a more brilliant, enthusiastic and unanimous audience. The Duke of Cambridge presided, and many representatives of the peerage were there. The common folk thronged in too, and overflowed the hall, and formed a vast crowd surrounding the hall, eager to hear the eloquent speeches of appreciation, eager to support any proposal of a testimonial.

Someone (perhaps the Duke of Cambridge) said that

Miss Nightingale had always wished to establish and maintain in her own land an institution like Pastor Fliedner's at Kaiserswerth. Therefore let it be resolved that a "Nightingale Fund" be raised, which would enable her to have in England a nurses' training school. Every person at the meeting, almost every person in the British Isles agreed to this suggestion. Mr. Sidney Herbert sent Miss Nightingale a copy of the resolution and told her how freely the contributions were already being made.

After receiving these communications, Florence answered rather coolly. She had not been especially pleased to learn of all the fuss and hubbub in England; she had never really wanted a public meeting held to pay her homage. She was, of course, not unmindful of the sympathy and the confidence which originators of the scheme had shown her—but unless she was to have sole control of the Nightingale Fund and the English Kaiserswerth she would not be interested. She would accept the proposal, yes. But her present work was such as she would never leave for any other. "I accept their proposal, provided I may do so on their understanding of this great uncertainty as to when it will be possible for me to carry it out."

Did she seem ungracious? She did not mean to. Perhaps it was only that she alone realized what she strove for—which was not recognition, but the feeling of having done God's will properly, in her own way—and *enough*.

16

ADVENTURE'S ENDING

SEVASTOPOL FELL TO the British and French armies September 8, 1855. This ending of the siege was really the close of the Crimean War. There would be a few more skirmishes before the signing of the peace in Paris the following March; but with the capitulation of beleaguered Sevastopol, Russia knew that she was defeated and her troops beat a gradual retreat.

The war was over—and what good was ever to be derived from all the fighting and bloodshed, perhaps no one in the world could say. But, anyway, it was over. Through the autumn months, Britain's expeditionary force was removed, bit by bit, from the Crimean peninsula and shipped back home.

But, as usual, the terrible aftermath of war remained to be dealt with; the maimed and mutilated men, the invalids in the Crimean and Scutari hospitals. These victims Florence Nightingale still regarded as her charge. Many friends, the members of her family, implored her to resign her position now and return to England. The Bracebridges, feeling that the pressure of work had slackened, were leaving—

"Please, Flo, come with us! You are not half so well as you pretend; your health is not what it was before that bout with the fever in the spring. Please, dear," said Selina, "let somebody else shoulder the burdens here!"

But Florence was not to be persuaded. True to an old promise, Aunt Mai Smith was starting for Scutari. "I'm staying, Selina," said Florence. "Aunt Mai will take your place as my special deputy. She will watch over me and my health."

Aunt Mai, arriving on the heels of the Bracebridges' departure, found her mission an arduous one. In letters she described the Lady-in-Chief's nightly activities, "She habitually writes till 1 or 2, sometimes till 3 or 4. We seldom get through even our little dinner (after it has been put off one, two or three hours on account of her visitors) without her being called away from it. I never saw a greater picture of exhaustion than Flo last night at ten . . . and she sat up the greater part of the night."

Such things as food, rest, temperature, Aunt Mai noticed, never interfered with Florence's performance of the task in hand. "She has attained a most wonderful calm and presence of mind. She is, I think, often deeply impressed, and depressed, though she does not show it outwardly. No irritation of temper, no hurry or confusion of manner, ever appears for a moment."

If she was depressed, it was because Florence foresaw that the winter would be harsh—in some respects, the difficulties might be even more numerous than those of a year ago. And so they were. Lord Raglan was dead now, an elderly man who had been worn out by the struggles and privations of the war. By some strange omission, the private and official instructions sent to him and defining exactly Miss Nightingale's position as superintendent of nurses had been mislaid or lost; and his successors, either indifferent or hostile to Miss Nightingale, said they knew nothing at all about it. Florence surmised that henceforth her work would be made as hard as possible for her; still, she could write pluckily to Mrs. Bracebridge, "We get things done all the same— only a little more slowly."

She had to go on horseback

Most of that winter she was in the Crimea. The weather was bad, with much snow, and she had to go on horseback or in a mule cart from one to another of the hospitals. It was hazardous traveling, and once the cart in which she rode upset among the ruts and snowdrifts, and she was tumbled out, battered and bruised. After this accident, she asked for and was given a hooded baggage car, without springs but drawn by a stout, sure-footed team, in which to make her rounds.

As she had expected, the several doctors and military officers who could never reconcile themselves to the Bird tried stubbornly to outwit and thwart her. But they had reckoned without Miss Nightingale's own stubbornness. She would not be outwitted or thwarted. She would not be stopped.

On one occasion, the enemy faction in a Balaclava hospital actually locked the doors against her—locked her out in the winter cold. She got a chair and sat down near the locked door, and having sent off a messenger for another key, she sat there all day, waiting, until at night the key was fetched. Then she went in. She was angry, yes. But she would have sat in that spot forever, if necessary, to gain entrance to the patients behind the door.

Sometimes the persecution took other forms; she had little or no food; her nurses had no beds and must sleep on benches in the office of a barrack. Perhaps the opposition thought such treatment would drive the Bird away. But she stayed, ignoring these things, as she said, *"for the sake of the work."*

"When people offend, they offend the Master before they do me," she said; therefore she would not "kick" or resist or resent, for that was not the Master's command. And, she added, "Is it even common sense?" She did not believe so.

By contrast were the reports reaching her from England where she seemed to be constantly more famous. The Nightingale Fund was growing enormously; the

Crimean soldiers had subscribed nearly £9,000, the Navy and Coast Guard almost as much. Jenny Lind had sung a benefit concert, the proceeds of which were contributed to the Fund.

In November Queen Victoria wrote Florence a letter filled with phrases of warmest admiration. "I am anxious, however," said the Queen, "of marking my feelings in a manner which I trust will be agreeable to you, and send you with this letter a brooch, the form and emblems of which commemorate your great and blessed work, and which I hope you will wear as a mark of the high approbation of your Sovereign!"

The brooch, a large enamelled badge, was stamped with St. George's Cross and the Royal Cipher, surmounted by a crown of diamonds and the word "Crimea." Around the edge was an inscription, "Blessed are the Merciful;" and on the reverse surface was a second inscription: "To Miss Florence Nightingale, as a mark of esteem and gratitude for her devotion to the Queen's brave soldiers. From Victoria R. 1855."

Florence had little taste for jewelry; her costumes were always unadorned, extremely simple; but she was proud of having earned her Sovereign's "high approbation," and so she wore the brooch Christmas Day when she went to dine at the British Embassy in Constantinople. It was a distinguished company, the men in colorful uniforms, the women beautifully and fashionably gowned—yet, somehow, Miss Nightingale in her white cap and plain black dress, the Queen's decoration at her throat, was the center of attraction, all eyes turned to her.

"I felt quite dumb," wrote another of the guests later, "as I looked at her wasted figure and short brown hair combed over the forehead like a child's. She is very

slight, rather above the middle height; her face is long
and thin, but this may be from recent illness and great
fatigue. She has a very prominent nose, slightly Roman;
and small grey eyes, kind, yet penetrating; but her face
does not give you at all the idea of great talent. She looks
a quiet, persevering, orderly, lady-like woman. She was
still very weak and did not join in the games, but she
sat on a sofa and looked on, laughing until the tears came
into her eyes."

The weather moderated in March. Often on those
early spring days Florence would stroll for an hour in
the English burying-ground at Scutari. Many of her
nurses had gone home now, the major part of the troops
had gone and hundreds of convalescents; the hospitals
were no longer crowded. But here were the soldiers who
were never to see England again, it was of them Florence
thought most earnestly—the dead.

Which among them had died needlessly? This was the
question she brooded on; the needless deaths resulting
from neglect and inadequacy of preparation and equipment. She remembered the shiploads of men brought
from the battlefields, how poorly they had been clothed,
how poorly nourished. That they should have suffered so
was inexcusable; it was a wicked extravagance which
should have been checked at the source. She had studied
and pondered; and she had determined that what had
happened in the Crimea must never recur. No other
British soldiers must ever know such cruel treatment,
such a tragic fate.

Something must be done! What? Perhaps the whole
policy of a nation in regard to the maintaining of its
armies must be revised, the whole system of the British

War Department be reformed. A colossal undertaking? Yes, but it could be effected.

Strolling, meditating, Florence Nightingale made a solemn vow—to herself and to God. Something would surely be done.

By midsummer the hospitals were almost empty, the four miles of corridors and wards at the Barrack, where wounded men had strained to catch a glimpse of a lady's flickering lamp, were deserted and echoing. The last duty had been discharged. Florence was sailing for England.

The British government had begged her to accept the use of a man-of-war for the voyage; she had said no, politely; she preferred to travel without flourish or pomp. She had reserved passage on a French ship and had signed the register as "Miss Smith." On the very day before leaving, she arranged for a huge cross of white marble to be erected on the mountain heights above Balaclava, on a peak not far from the sanatorium where she had lain so ill. This was to be her own tribute to the war's heroes, a shining cross with, at the foot, the carved supplication: "Lord have mercy on us."

With Aunt Mai and as "Miss Smith," she boarded the vessel. She had made no announcements of any sort, intended making none. In her portfolio was a letter which said that the regiments of the Coldstream Guards, the Grenadiers and the Fusiliers would send their three bands to meet her at the station and "play her home, whenever she might arrive, whether by day or night, if only they could find out when." But, wanting no bands, she had not told anyone about her journey.

From the French seaport she went to Paris, stopped for a night in a modest hotel and then was off to London.

"Miss Smith" was so inconspicuous in London that her true identity was never guessed. She got on a train which took her to the village station of Whatstandwell, and from there she walked alone to Lea Hurst.

She crossed the terrace of the big old stone house and rang the bell. The butler admitted her.

"Is it—it *is* Miss Florence!"

"Yes," she said. "I'm home."

"Certain persons have come in advance, Miss Florence. William Jones, a one-legged sailor lad; and Peter, a very little Russian boy—Peter Grillage, he calls himself. And a dog, Miss Florence; Rousch, a black Crimean puppy."

She smiled. "The spoils of war. I've said I would adopt William Jones and Peter Grillage; they have no people. The black puppy was given to me by the soldiers in the Barrack."

"They're all here. Miss Parthe is caring for them."

The butler bowed and stood aside, and she went past him—into the Lea Hurst drawing-room and the embrace of her parents and sister.

17

A NEW SUMMONS

"Now," Parthe said, "all that terrible time is behind you, Flo. Now you can rest."

They were in the morning room at Lea Hurst, Florence stretched out on a divan, scarcely listening to her sister's conversation, thinking not of what was behind but of what was ahead, a job to be done, a hard job—and how had she best attack it? In her diary only a few days ago, she had written, "I stand at the altar of the murdered men, and while I live I fight their cause." She had never meant anything more sincerely. Oh, how she hated stupidity, the false economy which had wasted so many lives, the false pride which would not correct its mistakes of judgment. With the Derbyshire sun cheerfully shining at the windows, she walked in memory the frosty winter corridors of Scutari, a lamp in her hand, the flickering rays playing upon bleakness and agony.

Parthe went on, "You can't imagine the people who have come to Lea Hurst this week, in carriages and on foot, hoping to see you. Hordes of people. The village is positively overrun. And all the lovely gifts! The workmen at Sheffield have sent you a set of beautiful cutlery; and there's that fine desk sent by our county neighbors. But I think the Duke of Devonshire's present is the very nicest —a silver owl! Quite like dear old Athena, this silver owl is; we must show it to Athena when we go to Embley. Flo, no other British subject has ever equaled your popularity. It is simply astounding!"

Florence smiled wryly. "At Scutari there were moments when the officials, to a man, would have burned me like Joan of Arc. But they knew they couldn't, and knew the War Office would not turn me out, because the English public was with me."

The butler entered with the mail. Since Miss Florence's arrival, the butler had obtained a bigger tray for the mail which was of tremendous proportions, stacks of letters and packages every day, and most of them addressed to this most popular of British subjects. Parthe took the letters and sorted them.

"Here is one from Sir James Clark in Scotland, Flo."

"Open it," Florence said. "Read it to me."

Parthe read. Sir James was asking Miss Nightingale and her father to be his guests during September at his house near Balmoral. He added that the Queen would be in residence then at Balmoral Castle close by; and the Queen had said she hoped to see Miss Nightingale.

Florence sat up suddenly. She recalled something which the Queen had said in the letter accompanying the jeweled badge, "It will be a very great satisfaction to me, when you return at last to these shores, to make the acquaintance of one who has set so bright an example to our sex." Would not this be the ideal opportunity to interest Victoria in the scheme which was obsessing all Florence's thoughts?

"Parthe, I shall accept Sir James's invitation!"

"But *can* you, Flo? Have you the strength to go to Scotland?"

"Of course, I'm going," said Florence. "It's a wonderful chance."

Lying there resting (or so, at least, Parthe believed) Florence thought of a scheme she had recently been devising. It was a thing so ambitious that any other person might well have shrunk from contemplating it. But Florence Nightingale was made of sterner stuff. She would be faithful to the vow repeated so often in the burying-ground above the Barrack in Scutari; what had happened must never happen again and the bitter lessons of the Crimea must be instilled now, before time swept the war into oblivion.

What would it mean to keep the vow? She did not know. But whatever it meant, that could be done. And must be!

She would need backing and reenforcements. She would be the Lady-in-Chief, but there would have to be captains to command, men distinguished and in high place, men she could count on.

Who? Well, Sidney Herbert. Yes, she could always count on him; like herself, his one thought was to establish God's kingdom on earth. Service was a religion to him, as it was to her. Dr. John Sutherland was another of the same stripe—Dr. Sutherland, the London physician who had been a member of the sanitation commission dispatched by Lord Shaftesbury to Scutari. Florence had liked Dr. Sutherland and recognized in him the reformer's temperament.

These two, then, to start with. And more, later.

Mr. William Shore Nightingale and his daughter Florence went to Sir James Clark's home, Birk Hall, September 19, 1856; and two days later Sir James drove his

guests to Balmoral Castle and there introduced them to
Queen Victoria and her husband, the Prince Consort.

It is only good manners to prepare for an afternoon's
visit with royalty—Florence had prepared in more ways
than one. Ever since she had known it was in prospect,
she had resolved that this afternoon should be important,
to herself, her plans, the nation as a whole. In these last
several days she had been studying, poring over statistics, storing up information. When the Queen inquired
about her work, she was ready with detailed answers.

She pointed out the fact which had so impressed her,
that the soldiers were not properly cared for in peace
times, and therefore went, undernourished and poorly
clad and frequently half-sick, into war service. During
the first seven months of the Crimean campaign, the
mortality rate from disease alone had been sixty percent
—"a rate, Your Majesty, which exceeds that of the Great
Plague in London, a higher rate than the mortality in
cholera." But even more dreadful to contemplate, the
death rate among soldiers, young men between the ages
of twenty and thirty-five, in peace times was double the
civilian death rate—"in some London districts, the difference is much worse. Our soldiers enlist to death in the
barracks!"

Surely a royal commission should be ordered, to look
into the situation, and all the facilities which science and
education had developed should be employed to remedy
it. And immediately! Delay would be fatal. She denounced all who might advise delay.

"No one can feel for the army as I do. These people
who talk to us have all fed their children on the fat of the
land and dressed them in velvet and silk, while we have
been away. I have had to see *my* children dressed in a

dirty blanket and an old pair of regimental trousers, and see them fed on raw, salt meat, and nine thousand of my children—from causes which might have been prevented —are now in their forgotten graves. But I can never forget! People must have seen that long winter to know what it was!"

Miss Nightingale's eloquence was very moving; she spoke with intense emotion, and Queen Victoria believed her. A royal commission? But in England, a constitutional monarchy, the Crown cannot institute reforms which have not originated with its ministers. This, said the Queen, was something Lord Panmure, the Secretary of State for War, must sponsor. Since Lord Panmure was expected at Balmoral within the week, Miss Nightingale must stay and talk with him. Lord Panmure must be persuaded, and the Queen thought this could be more easily done if she herself were there to aid in the persuading.

Florence was not so optimistic about Lord Panmure. She had written to him just after her return from Scutari, wanting to put her suggestions before him, and his reply had been polite enough but very evasive. But if the Queen wished it, she would wait at Balmoral for him, and hope for the best.

That night, the Prince Consort wrote in his journal of Miss Nightingale's visit, "We are much pleased with her; she is extremely modest."

The Queen, in a letter to the Duke of Cambridge, wrote a comment which was destined to become a classic: "Such a clear head. I wish we had her at the War Office."

Florence's first encounter with Lord Panmure was, it seemed, a successful one. He was a large, burly Scotsman, with thick shoulders, a shaggy head, and a way of moving slowly and ponderously. Florence promptly nicknamed him the "Bison," and called him that in her letters

Promptly renamed him The Bison

to Sidney Herbert with whom she was in constant communication. She conferred with the Bison both at Balmoral and at Birk Hall; and it was agreed that she should write a report of her Crimean experiences, with notes on necessary reforms, this document to be considered by the cabinet. Soon after her departure from Scotland, Florence heard what the Bison's opinion of her had been in these meetings. Sir James Clark's son wrote to Miss Nightingale, "You may like to know that you fairly overcame Pan. We found him with his mane absolutely silky, and a loving sadness pervading his whole being." And Sidney Herbert wrote, "I forget whether I told you that the Bison was very much pleased with his interview with you. He says that he was very much surprised at your physical appearance, as I think you must have been with his."

"Perhaps," mused Florence, "Lord Panmure has pictured all lady reformers as freaks."

When the Bison's request had been seconded by Lord Palmerston, the Prime Minister, Florence launched at once into the assembling of material for her report. She went to London and took rooms at the Burlington Hotel in Old Burlington Street. Aunt Mai Smith accompanied her; and Florence gave her parents and Parthe to understand that she wanted no other chaperonage. As she had foreseen, this separation from her family aroused protests—especially from Mrs. Nightingale, who had fondly hoped that after so many adventures, Florence would now step back into the role of a dutiful daughter at home. But, having tasted freedom from family bonds, Florence had no intention of being trapped by them again.

As a matter of fact, her discontent at being at home, her resentment of any family claims made upon her, seemed to deepen as she grew older—perhaps because she thought of herself as an agent for service rather than as a woman, perhaps because she had not in her nature the longing for affection and warm personal relationships which most women know. Her capacity for love was great, but it was reserved for the human race, for the poor and abused and underprivileged; she chose not to expend it on individuals. The work she had done, and had still to do, was always uppermost in her heart and brain; she lived for that alone; everything else was superfluous, a distraction, every moment missed from her work an extravagance—almost a sin.

Friends were valuable only as they could be used to advance her work. Aunt Mai and Uncle Sam Smith were valuable because of their undeviating obedience to the demands of their niece's work. Her father she would see occasionally, in gratitude for the sympathy he had never failed to extend. As for Mamma and Parthe, they had not approved of Florence's work in the old days; and though their plaintiveness had melted away in the bright glow of her fame, they probably didn't approve of the work now. She felt that she owed them no debt of any sort. Obviously, she was not obliged to share existence with them.

Once settled in the Burlington Hotel (with Aunt Mai posted as a bodyguard, to keep off the curious folk who always haunt a celebrity) Florence began the selection of men she wanted as members of a royal commission to put through her reforms. Sidney Herbert must be chairman—she was sure of that! But the others must be painstakingly examined and each one pledged to carry out her ideas. As she had said, and as she honestly believed, no one on earth could "feel for the army" as she did, no one knew so well the faults in the present system. After weeks of correspondence and consultations, weeks in which her hotel apartment came to be known as the "Little War Office," she completed her roster of commissioners; and when at length Lord Panmure called on her, she was able to persuade him to the appointment of all but one of her nominees.

This in itself was a triumph; and much encouraged, Florence proceeded to write the report Lord Panmure had asked for.

A voluminous thing, that report! A monumental labor, a manuscript thousands of pages long, a full account of Florence's experiences in the Crimean War, but more than that—a medical history of the war, with chapters of figures and statistics and sections dealing with army diet and cookery, washing and canteens, commissariats and provisioning agents, the construction of army hospitals, the education and promotion of medical officers. No phase of those problems faced and solved at Scutari was omitted from the report; and in the final section the Lady-in-Chief summarized her suggestions for reform.

But though Florence wrote at prodigious length, she had finished before Lord Panmure was ready to name the royal commissioners. The Bison, she discovered, was indeed a slow-moving animal. To Florence, with her vigorous disposition and sharp temper, this tendency to procrastinate was maddening.

For months then she applied herself, with Sidney Herbert's connivance, to a process which she described as "bullying the Bison." She wanted action—at once; whereas the Bison seemed to have an aversion even to the thought of action. "Appoint the commissioners *now*!" she begged; the Bison answered that he had the gout in his hands, he could not write. Gout in his hands? Florence was enraged. "It is the flimsiest of excuses. Keep on bullying him!" she said to Mr. Herbert. "Threaten him. Tell him that unless he acts today, you will resign the chairmanship!" Mr. Herbert threatened—and the Bison only grunted.

But Florence held the trump card in this political game, and in the spring of 1857 she decided to use it. Suppose she should herself publish the story of the Crimean campaign—publish it from the housetops, so that the world would know of the British government's sins against the British army? She sent word to Lord Panmure that she would brook no further delay. "Sir, I shall go to the country with my story!"

As the Bison very well knew, the country was with Miss Nightingale. The last thing he could afford was to find himself pitted against her in a public airing of her cause. For Miss Nightingale was right. Simple justice was on her side. She was right, and the career of any man who opposed her now was at stake and would be forfeited.

So the Bison stirred. The Royal Warrant was issued, the commissioners named, the commission started its operations.

At her headquarters in Old Burlington Street, Florence chalked up another triumph. She had forced this action. But she was rather sure that her report would never be published, and therefore she arranged to have it printed and privately circulated at her own expense, as a matter of record—and as an instrument which, perhaps, she might have to use again.

She determined to see to it that the commission did not adopt Lord Panmure's tactics, but should push through its inquiry with all possible speed.

18

MORE LAMPS LIGHTED

WITH THE APPOINTMENT of the royal commission, Florence had made the first step in her program of reform. During the summer of 1857, she busied herself with the second step—that of forcing the commission to accept the specific aims set forth in her report. Four things she demanded: all army barracks must be rendered sanitary and livable; an army statistical department must be organized; an army medical school must be instituted; the entire army medical department must be revolutionized and reconstructed and all existing army hospital regulations revised to conform with her own scientific ideas. She could not, of course, be a member of the commission; as a woman, she was barred from any open participation in its labors. But she could control it—remaining behind the scenes and working through Sidney Herbert, Dr. Sutherland and the other commissioners, all of whom, with one exception, were sworn to her cause.

She was conscious of her powers. Not only was the Queen her avowed ally, but she had also the masses of the British people adoring and trusting her. Besides, she had so impressed herself upon the public mind that she was spoken of everywhere as infallibly versed in all questions of public service. The common belief was that whatever your problem, Miss Nightingale could solve it for you. She was wise, she was good, she had the love of humanity in her heart; and her experience was unlimited. Little wonder then that pioneers in every conceivable type of reform came to her with their own pet theories, asking for help, or that statesmen sought and deferred to her opinions.

She listened to what they said

They came to the Burlington Hotel, all these people who wished to see Miss Nightingale, and they waited in lines outside her door, hoping for the chance. Most of them she received, for a half-hour at a time; she listened to what they said and noted any of it that seemed sensible. If any man who might be of assistance to her stayed away, she sent for him—and he came as quickly as he could. She talked with the great and the near-great; England's Prime Minister was not too proud or too busy to respond to her summons.

Sidney Herbert was in consultation with her every day, and Dr. Sutherland quite as often. Indeed, these three composed the inner "cabinet" of Florence's "Little War Office"; and between the intervals of her larger meeting with an ever-increasing company of medical and social scientists, the small "cabinet" was in almost constant session. Yet even so, the Lady-in-Chief sometimes felt that Mr. Herbert and Dr. Sutherland could, if they tried, exert themselves a bit more in her behalf, and at such times she chided them.

Mr. Herbert had long ago acknowledged Florence as his guiding star and never protested. But Dr. Sutherland, a big jovial man, twenty years her senior, would on occasion tease her in fatherly vein about her impatience. "My dear Lady," he wrote once, replying to an angry note from Florence, "do not be unreasonable. I would have been with you yesterday, but, alas, my will was stronger than my legs. I have been at the Commission today, and as yet there is nothing to fear. I was too fatigued and too stupid to see you afterwards, but I intend coming tomorrow about 12 o'clock, and we can then prepare for the campaign of the coming week."

But if she seemed to drive these friends incontinently, she was no less exacting with herself. As Selina Brace-bridge had said so long ago, Florence was not as well as she pretended to be and she began to show the strain of raddled nerves.

She had gone to Embley for Christmas and again for a few days in the spring—but her work had followed her there. Parthe declared that she quite hated the sight of the post with its long official envelopes addressed to Florence. But to Florence the official envelopes were an essential, the tools of her trade. Compared with what she was doing now, all she had accomplished at Scutari was the merest child's play, she said. Let Parthe and Mamma and Papa worry about her, if they must. That was not important. Only her work was important. There were many times when she was so exhausted that she lay for hours on the sofa in a sort of stupor, eyes shut, face pallid, scarcely breathing, as if she had fainted dead away—but if anyone dared say she was too ill for work, she would leap up and burst forth in tempestuous denial.

As the summer wore on and her health became worse, Dr. Sutherland pleaded with her to slacken the furious pace. With good-natured affection he told her that she was interested in everybody's sanitary improvement but her own. "Pray leave us all to ourselves, soldiers and all, for a while," he said. "We shall all be the better for a rest." Sidney Herbert added his voice to the argument, wouldn't she stop for a brief vacation? "I wish you could be turned into a cross-country squire like me for a few weeks!"

But no, she would not rest, would not stop. Instead, she started a new project, that of preparing a document in which she accounted for the administration of all funds and gifts sent to her during the war. She was taut with nerves, like a fine coiled spring that has been wound too tightly. Why, why, she cried, did people keep *pecking* at her? These admonitions, these warnings were echoes from the drawing-rooms of Embley and Lea Hurst; she had heard them since she was a child; and she would have none of them.

By autumn her illness was so marked that she at last consented to go to Malvern for treatment at the sanatorium there. Aunt Mai was her companion. When Malvern seemed not to benefit Florence, the two went on to other health resorts, dragging wearily from place to place. The doctors who examined her at this time were baffled by her case. Organically, they said, she was sound; but the years of over-exertion had shattered her nervous system; the doctors feared she must be an incurable invalid for the remainder of her life.

An incurable invalid? Florence was irate at the pronouncement. Learning in November that nurses were needed for the army in India, she wrote to volunteer her services—an offer made when she scarcely had strength to stand alone and, fortunately, the offer was refused.

A month later, Florence became convinced that she would soon die, and she set about ordering her affairs. She wrote a letter to Sidney Herbert outlining a course of action by which he could carry through her reforms, and expressing regret that she could not stay alive to "do the nurses," and to spend the money in the Florence Nightingale Fund with which she had hoped to found a training-school for her profession. Her inheritance she was leaving for the building of modern barracks, she said. She wrote also to Parthe, directing the disposal of all her personal belongings and keepsakes and asking that she be buried in the Crimea. She was sad at the thought of approaching death, but resigned to it because it seemed God's plan. "Perhaps He wants a 'Sanitary Officer' now for my Crimeans in some other world where they are gone."

She was still in her suite at the Old Burlington, for she preferred to die there in the midst of her work, rather than at either of her father's homes. But the weeks and the months passed and she did not die—and presently she was almost magically revived by the publication of the Royal Commission's report. Miss Nightingale's advice had been followed in every detail by the men whose appointments she had secured. Well, now that these things had been recommended, they must be put into effect!

Immediately she launched into this task, the final step in her program. Thin and white, propped up with pillows in her bed, she flung herself into the new work, writing, writing, studying charts and graphs, compiling statistics, calling statesmen to her for conferences—with slender, delicate fingers manipulating the policies of an empire.

In June, 1858, Parthe married Sir Harry Verney. The event meant little to Florence who was engrossed in matters of national portent and, as Aunt Mai said, working as if "each day may be the last on which she will have power to work." Writing to a friend, Florence commented that Parthe liked the marriage—"which is the main thing. And my father is very fond of Sir Harry Verney, which is the next best thing. He is old and rich, which is a disadvantage. He is active, has a will of his own and four children ready made, which is an advantage. So, on the whole, I think these reflections tend to approbation."

Perhaps the truth was that Florence had grown so far from her family that she could be touched only lightly by anything happening within the family circle. Parthe and her mother were almost like strangers to her; she had asked them not to come to the Old Burlington on their London visits, lest they disturb her at her work; and it was only infrequently that she ventured to Embley for a day or two, traveling in an invalid's conveyance and waited upon by Aunt Mai or by her friend, Mr. Arthur Clough, the poet, who had recently attached himself to Miss Nightingale's staff, somewhat in the role of errand boy or general factotum. With her father, Florence was more lenient, permitting him to call upon her at the hotel whenever he was in London. ("Dear Papa," she wrote, "I shall always be well enough to see *you* while this mortal coil is on me at all.") By special appointment, and sometimes as often as twice a day, he would slip into her room and sit beside the bed, talking to her for a full half-hour about religion and philosophy, those subjects which had always so fascinated him.

Now and then Hilary Bonham Carter came, or some other cousin, or the Bracebridges or Madame Mohl; and all were allowed a glimpse of Florence, leaning back among her pillows, and the counterpane covered with books, notebooks, writing paraphernalia. But mostly she saw only such persons as were working with her.

She did not see a great deal even of Aunt Mai who, as Parthe said, was the "dragon," posted outside her niece's bedchamber, warding off interlopers.

To an extent, and in a queer way, physical weakness became a protection to Florence, a haven from the interruptions and distractions which fret one who leads a more normal life, an economy measure to conserve time and energy. Uncle Sam Smith was in charge of her finances; she never had to bother about money or bills, for Uncle Sam made sure that she was comfortably maintained in the Burlington suite. Dr. Sutherland was always at hand, assuming the position of confidential secretary and taking over many taxing small duties. A request to speak to Miss Nightingale must first be scanned by Dr. Sutherland, who judged whether or not the request might be worthy of her attention. She saw no one whom she wished not to see; and yet she could turn away petitioners without offense, since it was well known that she was an invalid, struggling to perform a splendid and gigantic work and constantly working beyond her actual strength. There was Mr. Clough too, who asked for nothing more than the reward of serving Florence—in any way at all, who was happy just to fetch the mail, or write her inconsequential letters, or do up packages, or escort her on infrequent excursions in a closed carriage through the park.

To the British people at large Miss Nightingale was a lovely symbol, almost a legendary figure, a woman who had sacrificed (and continued to sacrifice) her youth, her ease, the pleasures of society, even her health in the cause of mercy. It was understood that she did not now appear in public, yet ever and again the rumor would get about that she *had* appeared, in the streets, in a restaurant or music hall. Then the woman who faintly resembled Miss Nightingale, who had been taken for her, would be surrounded by worshipful, sentimental throngs of folk who stretched out their hands to her, crying, "Let me stroke your shawl, ma'am! Please, ma'am, let me touch the hem of your skirt!"

When told of such incidents, Florence was humbly grateful—and vaguely irritated. She had never coveted fame or applause. She knew that she possessed genius, but she used it for the relief of God's creatures and she felt that she deserved no thanks.

Though she had many strings to her bow, many men of high rank in the realm at her beck and call, there was none like Sidney Herbert—probably history has never known a more unusual friendship than theirs. The association had in it no hint of romance; Mr. Herbert was happily married and his wife was that person whom Florence always addressed as "my dearest." Yet no two comrades ever shared so completely in ideals, ambitions and purposes as did Florence Nightingale and Sidney Herbert. On every question they saw eye-to-eye; together they saw each question whole, the talents of one supplementing the talents of the other.

Both were reformers born and bred; both were intensely religious; but of the two, Florence was the leader. Brave, chivalrous, unselfish and charming though he was, Sidney Herbert lacked the obstinate, ruthless, almost fanatical zeal which was so much a part of Florence's character. He regarded her as his superior in all things; she commanded and he obeyed. Several hours of every day he spent with her, and the times between their meetings he interspersed with notes and messages.

19

HEROINE'S PROGRESS

So SUPERBLY DID Florence manage her campaign that by 1861 every one of her proposed reforms had been effected and a new era in the welfare and efficiency of the British army had dawned. In the future there would be no such cruelties of neglect as had been endured by the troops in the Crimea. From this time forward, British soldiers wherever they were, would be quartered in barracks and hospitals which were correctly heated and lighted; their water supply would be ample and pure; their food would be properly cooked and their health constantly supervised.

Florence Nightingale was responsible for all these changes. Yet, having brought them into being, she was still not quite satisfied. The War Office itself had not been reorganized; she saw it as an old, outmoded, creaking machine, tied around with red tape which she had always detested—and she determined that it, too, must be reformed!

During most of the five-year period since her return from the Crimea, Sidney Herbert had been Secretary for War in the British cabinet, the indefatigable champion of all reform measures; and to him Florence now looked for assistance in her latest endeavor. Florence, in her sanctuary at the Burlington Hotel, would draw up the plans, which Mr. Herbert must then put into practice.

Root and branch, the War Office must be modernized; Florence did not doubt that together she and Sidney Herbert could bring it about.

There was, of course, antagonism from the start. Those men who had for years served in the War Office were instantly suspicious and set themselves to resist the reorganization. One among them, Sir Benjamin Hawes, the permanent Under-Secretary, was especially unfriendly to the idea of change.

"Our scheme," said Florence, "will probably result in Ben Hawes' resignation, and that is another of its advantages."

But Ben Hawes himself had no notion of resigning—not, at least, without a battle. He had long been a fixture in his job and meant to stay.

In the midst of the preliminary skirmishing, which Florence thoroughly enjoyed, Sidney Herbert suddenly fell ill. Or perhaps his illness was not so sudden, after all, for he had never been a physically robust man; he had been working without respite, and a year earlier he had been severely stricken with pleurisy. Anyway, he now was so far from well that doctors told him he must retire from public life, he must rest—or risk a total breakdown.

No news could have seemed more disastrous to Florence Nightingale, and she received it first with skepticism and then with resentment. Sidney Herbert retiring because of illness? But that was absurd! She herself had been ill all this while—so ill, indeed, that she scarcely ever rose from her bed! Yet she had never once thought of stopping work. Did the doctors say that Sidney Herbert had a fatal disease? What nonsense! "You know," exclaimed Florence, "I don't believe in fatal diseases." She sent for him and he came to consult with her, and she told him that he could not rest until the War Office had been reformed; the goal was so near, so very near, that he could not turn back now. He had been created a baron recently and as Lord Herbert he was entitled to a seat in the House of Lords. Why not, said Florence, give up his seat in the House of Commons and seek the comparative quiet of the House of Lords, remaining at the War Office, but taking things at a more leisurely stride?

Herbert reluctantly assented to this compromise. He would do as Florence said.

She was delighted. "One fight more," she cried, "the best and the last!"

So, for several more months, the fight went on—with Sidney Herbert's condition growing steadily weaker. Now he was attacked by fainting fits, and there were days when it was only by sipping brandy that he could keep on his feet. He listened as Florence spurred him on, cheering and encouraging him; but he knew finally that he had reached the end of his efforts. He would never be able to reform the War Office; and the dreadful moment had arrived when he must go to Florence and tell her of his failure.

He wrote out his resignation, and on July 9 he called at Florence's hotel to bid her good-bye before his departure for a hospital at Spa. Florence greeted him coldly, with reproaches. He said sadly that he was beaten.

"Beaten?" she repeated. "Don't you see that you've simply thrown away the game? And with all the winning cards in your hands! And so noble a game! Sidney Herbert beaten! Beaten by Ben Hawes! It is a disgrace—a worse disgrace than the hospitals at Scutari!"

This was their farewell, for he was never to see her again. On July 25 he was removed from Spa to his palatial and beloved home at Wilton, where a week later he died. His last murmurings before he lapsed into unconsciousness were of Florence.

This was their farewell

"Poor Florence! Poor Florence! Our joint work unfinished!"

What was her reaction to this calamity? She was wild with grief, she was inconsolable. Sidney Herbert dead? Gone—gone beyond recall? It could not be true!

But it was true, and when the fact was borne in upon her, she stifled her sobs and wrote long letters in praise of him, extolling his virtues as a friend, a Christian, an English gentleman. She wrote a memorandum on his achievements as an army reformer and sent this paper to Mr. Gladstone so that it might become a public record for all to read. Everything she herself had accomplished owed its success to Sidney Herbert, she said. Everything! He had been the "head and center" of it all. If remorse tinged her sorrow, if she felt that she had in any way hastened his collapse, she did not say so; but always afterward, whether in writing or speaking she referred to Sidney Herbert as her "dear master" and cherished his image in her heart.

The months which followed were difficult for Florence. Twice more misfortune struck at her. Arthur Clough died the next spring, a genuine bereavement, for the poet in his modest, self-effacing manner had made himself almost indispensable, each day doing dozens of small services and kindnesses to accommodate Miss Nightingale and lighten her burdens. Perhaps she hadn't sufficiently appreciated Arthur Clough or the quality of his devotion while he lived; but when he died she sorely missed him. She could not bear to open a newspaper lest she see his name in print and be reminded of her loss; and she sometimes wondered dismally whether she hadn't relied too much upon him and been "a drag upon his health and spirits."

Grief of another but no less poignant sort came to her from the most unexpected of all sources—from Aunt Mai Smith who, shortly after Clough's death, said that she must leave Florence and live again with her own family.

This to Florence seemed desertion—nothing else!—and she was wrathful. In vain Aunt Mai explained her reasons; she was now sixty-three years old, she said, and felt that she had earned a rest; her children and husband needed her; she wanted to be at home rather than posted, a "dragon," outside Florence's closed door. For these last four years, though every day in written communication with her famous niece, and only a few paces away, Aunt Mai hadn't *seen* Florence even once to speak to! Probably the loneliness of such an assignment had palled upon Aunt Mai; at any rate, she asked to be released.

Well, Florence could not hold Aunt Mai against her will, but she interpreted her going as disloyalty, as proof that she totally lacked understanding of the lofty causes for which Florence toiled. Evidently the business of reform meant nothing to Aunt Mai or she could not thus throw it all over at the slightest pretext. What fools, what utterly worthless creatures women were! In a towering rage, Florence wrote to Madame Mohl, pouring out the bitterness of her feeling against Aunt Mai. "I am sick with indignation at what wives and mothers will do out of the most egregious selfishness. And people call it all maternal or conjugal affection and think it pretty to say so."

But Aunt Mai left, just the same; and it was not until a very long time afterward that the breach was healed— and then only partially.

To "save something from the wreckage," Florence plunged into her work. It was her infallible refuge; it could not die, deceive or disappoint her. It was all that mattered in the world, and there was plenty of it to do. She sank herself in work, knowing that unlike human relationships it could never betray her.

Her activities during the ensuing few years were so many and varied as to defy enumeration, and to them all she brought that penetrating vision and intellectual skill which made certain their success.

The Civil War was then starting in the United States; and she was drawn into a correspondence with the American Secretary of War, advising him, providing him with statistics, rendering aid which was warmly welcomed and could not have been obtained elsewhere.

She published her *Notes on Nursing* and *Notes on Hospitals,* two detailed, instructive pamphlets which, printed and reprinted, were hailed as the clearest expositions on the subjects ever written, and were in reality the basis for all methods of modern treatment of the sick. No hospital was built in England without her inspection and approval of the plans.

She undertook and carried through to a victorious conclusion the introduction of sanitation in India, and the formation of a royal commission to do there what had been done for the British army at home. This was, if anything, a more enormous feat than any other she had attempted, a splendid labor of such scope as to affect and improve the lives of literally millions of people in that distant land where she had never been. She became the authority on all Indian matters for the British government; engineers and municipal officials sent her their plans for drainage and water facilities, and commissariat officials consulted her on soldiers' rations and victualing arrangements, and medical officers wrote to her for answers to their problems. Whatever progress was made in India was due in no small part to the imagination and sagacity of a bedridden woman in a London hotel room. For many years it was the custom for the newly appointed Viceroy, before he left England, to pay a visit to Miss Nightingale who would inform him concisely and accurately about the situation which he faced.

The foundation of the Nightingale Training School for Nurses was another event of this crowded, fruitful period. Since the time of its collection, the Nightingale fund had been invested in the name of a board of trustees, awaiting the moment when Florence should administer it.)Now she chose St. Thomas' Hospital in London as the location for her school; she mapped the courses of study and started the first classes. Though she did not go to the hospital to witness her nurses at their routine, she kept the strictest account of them and was familiar with everything they did. As the school settled into smooth-running order, its graduates went out, like a body of apostles, carrying with them the knowledge they had absorbed and proving to the world how well they had been trained.

As a natural sequel to her training of nurses, Florence turned next to the appalling need for reform in English workhouses and infirmaries. This had weighed upon her since the long-ago days when she had taught in the London Ragged Schools and observed the piteous straits of the great city's paupers and destitute. It was among such people that the old-fashioned nurses held sway— the drunken, blundering and often immoral attendants hired by thoughtless public officials to preside over public institutions and the indigent poor for whom nobody seemed to have any real concern and who were powerless to better their circumstances.

In Liverpool an experiment in district nursing was being made and, as usual, Miss Nightingale was solicited for advice. But in this case, she gave more than advice; she co-operated by sending twelve of her St. Thomas' nurses to Liverpool where they not only set up a system of district nursing but took charge of the workhouse and converted it to a model institution. Within ten years trained nurses were serving in infirmaries all over the country and the old, vicious methods had faded into obscurity.

At the same time, while directing the Liverpool venture, Florence was exerting pressure for the enactment of new Poor Laws, so that the former evils could never recur. In this, as in everything, she was successful. "From the first," said one of her fellow-workers, "I had a sort of fixed faith that Florence Nightingale could do anything, and that faith is still firm in me, and so it came to pass that the instant that name entered the lists I felt the fight was virtually won."

It was an age for reform in England. A corner seemed to have been turned, an era left behind. The public conscience was waking from old apathy, the desire to remedy old evils was everywhere, stirring, in the air; the inherent rights of the common man were coming to be recognized.

Perhaps even without Florence Nightingale some of these advancements might eventually have been realized —slowly, after long, damaging delays. But to Florence Nightingale must go full credit for hastening the processes of reform, setting them in motion and then pushing them relentlessly toward the climax which conquered all obstacles to progress. Stubborn and fiery she was, striving for perfection and pleased with nothing less, imbued herself with a demon of industry and having the godlike ability to transmit her fervor to others, the personal magnetism of an evangelist, the sweeping eloquence of an exhorter. Thus, she was the principal exponent, the mainspring of all good things which the years of reformation produced.

La Vie de Florence Rossignol . . . Writing each night in her diary, she must frequently have thought of the first slim volume in the series, that one written in schoolgirl French for the governess, dear Miss Christie. The life of Florence Nightingale? What a glorious chronicle it had become!

The story of a heroine . . .

20

AT HOME IN SOUTH STREET

FROM THE MOMENT of Sidney Herbert's death, Florence had been dissatisfied with her suite at the Burlington Hotel. Somehow, it seemed haunted by memories of him. She seemed always to see his handsome, courtly figure seated beside her, to hear his voice. Also the ghost of Arthur Clough was there ("He used to tell me how the leaves were coming out," she said, "knowing that, without his eyes, I should never see the spring again!")—and the imagined presence of Aunt Mai. These three who had been so helpful and now had gone. "I am glad," she wrote (most sorrowfully), "to end a day which can never come back, gladdest to end a month."

For several years she moved about, seeking a home of her own in which to settle down, finally taking a house at No. 10 South Street, which her father leased for her and which, except for rare intervals, she was to occupy for nearly a half-century.

The house was small and pleasant, rather like a tower in structure, having four floors besides basement and attic. On each floor were two rooms, a big one with large windows facing south, a little one with northern exposure. On the ground floor was a dining-room, lined with bookcases, and a sunny, balconied drawing-room, Victorian in style, with more bookcases and a sofa upon which Florence reclined whenever she ventured downstairs.

The second-floor rooms were literally filled with books, and boxes and cupboards of paper and files of correspondence which accumulated rapidly and were never destroyed. But Miss Nightingale's bedroom above was less businesslike and more attractive—a bright, airy, peaceful chamber with white walls and windows which had no blinds or curtains to keep out the light or obstruct the view. Here the furnishings were cheerful; a comfortable bed, tables and chairs conveniently located; pictures, a rose-shaded lamp, bowls of flowers sent up from the gardens at Embley and Lea Hurst in season.

On the top floor of the house was a guest room, and sometimes Florence had guests staying with her for a few days or a week. This did not necessarily mean that the guests were entertained personally by their hostess; usually they never laid eyes on her at all, but were granted the freedom of her hospitality—and read the notes she wrote them, which were brought by a maid or Dr. Sutherland.

As Florence said to Madame Mohl, "I am *obliged* (by my ill-health) to make Life an Art, to be always thinking of it; because otherwise I should do *nothing*."

The demands made upon her time and attention were constant, her mail was a vast flood of pamphlets, periodicals, letters. Her father had made her a liberal allowance, which was turned over to Mr. Sam Smith who paid the household accounts and distributed all surplus money at Florence's wish. Her way of living was so simple that she could give financial aid to many charities, and these she chose with care. But the begging letters, the appeals from every type of eccentric and crank, the ridiculous proposals of marriage which poured in upon her, Uncle Sam must deal with. The directions Florence scribbled to

Mr. Smith were characteristically definite: "Choke off this woman and tell her that I shall *never* be well enough to see her, here or *hereafter*."—"These miserable ecclesiastical quacks! Could you give them a lesson?"—"Dear Uncle Sam, please choke off this idiot."

All legitimate requests to see Miss Nightingale passed through the hands of Dr. Sutherland, who presided as her private secretary and chief steward in the drawing-room below. To Dr. Sutherland came at one time or another most of the dignitaries and celebrities, statesmen, scholars and politicians, reformers by the score, of England—and, indeed, of the civilized world—applying for an audience with the great lady whose approval or disapproval meant the difference between a cause's triumph or defeat. The truly unlucky applicants were those who never reached Miss Nightingale, whom Dr. Sutherland rejected at first glance. But what was the procedure for those more fortunate, upon whom Dr. Sutherland smiled rather than frowned?

Once told that you could see Miss Nightingale, a day and hour were set and you waited for your appointment. Then, at last, you were ushered to her upper room, you sat on a straight-backed chair at a proper distance from her bedside—she questioned you and you answered. Your conversation was strictly in the nature of an interview, nothing else, with no small talk, no wasted moments. You put your subject before Miss Nightingale, and almost instantly she had grasped it. Her mind was like a keen-edged knife cutting through complications to the gist of the matter. She might seem little and fragile lying there, but that was a deception. Only her body was fragile. Her intellect was quick, penetrating, strong; and whatever words you uttered had significance to her; she understood them, they were a part of her own information. You might have studied this thing, but you soon discovered that she too had studied it—and her knowledge probably went deeper than yours.

She might seem little and fragile

The conversation at an end, you rose and said goodbye and took yourself away, for there were others waiting, dozens of others, in a schedule divided for just such brief visits. And the lady must not be wearied!

One person at a time was admitted to the room. Miss

Nightingale received all her callers singly. For many years she never heard two other persons talking together or was included in a group where the talk was general. No person, even though a member of the household, ever entered the room by chance, no one ever appeared unexpectedly. If you saw Miss Nightingale at all, it was by express invitation and arrangement—and she, not you, determined the length of your visit.

When you were out of the room, you realized that quietly, courteously, tactfully, she had dismissed you. And that was that. Well, you would never forget her. Never!

After 1868 Florence toiled less strenuously at public reforms. The government had changed, many of her influential allies had retired; and though she still retained powerful contacts, she herself (as she phrased it) "went out of office." But she was industrious as ever, for now she could more closely supervise her training school for nurses.

This became her main activity. She saw to the moving of the institution to a better site, and then she took it in hand, much as if she were the headmistress of a girls' boarding school and the nurses her pupils.

She was very particular about the kind of young woman enrolling in training classes; she interviewed each candidate and it was only with her consent that one could be accepted. After these interviews, Miss Nightingale wrote down a memorandum of the impression made upon her by the visitor—what seemed to be this girl's attainments, what were her chances to be graduated and then to be useful in the world? Florence found such efforts gruelling and not always to her liking. "It takes a great deal out of me," she wrote to a friend. "God meant me for a reformer and I have turned out a detective." But it was, she thought, a duty which she must not shirk.

From her South Street home she exercised a remote control of all that went on in the school. Dr. Sutherland did the inspecting very regularly and thoroughly; from his reports, Florence drew her conclusions and checked upon the institution's welfare. She considered and dictated how the nurses should spend their holidays, she planned their futures, she had them come to her house, one at a time, for tea; she offered her guest room as a hostel for the matrons and teachers on their annual vacations.

She sent gifts of books and fruit to the nurses' dormitories and in summer the hospital was decorated with huge bouquets of rhododendrons from the Embley borders. Each January she wrote a New Year's address, which her brother-in-law, Sir Harry Verney, read aloud to the entire school in solemn assembly, in a hall garlanded with Lea Hurst evergreen boughs. The gentle wisdom of Miss Nightingale's words, delivered by Sir Harry, was a feature of the school calendar; and afterward, her address was printed and each nurse presented with a copy.

The detailed supervision lavished upon the students followed them as they went out into service; Florence kept her young women in sight, watching over them as a mother guards and guides her daughters. She corresponded with hundreds of them, receiving and answering thousands of letters every year from all corners of the globe where the Nightingale graduates were demonstrating the soundness of their training. Because of her efficiency and insistence upon an excellent preparation, the standards for nursing were raised throughout the British Empire and in many countries across the seas.

. She had a profound conviction about the work of nursing—which in time led to a prolonged debate with those experts who were promoting the movement for passage of a Nurses Registration Act.

To Florence, nursing was first and last a religious endeavor, as much so as the vocation of a nun; she was unalterably against any dissenting opinion, she had nothing but scorn for persons who regarded it as a business, she shrank from hearing it spoken of as a profession. A nurse, she said, should feel that hers was a high and sacred dedication, in which she was charged with the care of souls. Thus, moral and spiritual motives must be the nurse's best equipment, religious aims her vital quality. Such intangibles could never be *registered*, could they? No!—and the woman who looked at nursing as primarily a means of livelihood was not worthy of being a nurse at all!

The refuting argument to such reasoning might be that Miss Nightingale's experiences had been extraordinary; in her own case, the necessity of earning a livelihood had been absent. She could well afford to say that wages and salaries were no factor; she had known only conditions of financial security, even affluence; she had never been paid for her work and did not want or need to be paid— by contrast, she had donated large sums to the work from her large income. But, if her ideas prevailed, would not nursing soon be an endeavor—or a business, a profession —limited in membership only to women who had both leisure and wealth in combination with a religious inspiration? How many such women were there? Where were they to be found?

Though she fought bitterly in opposition, the majority of trained nurses came to endorse registration, and Florence had to bow to the inevitable. But she was unreconciled. The whole matter annoyed and grieved her—it was like those instances when one of the Nightingale nurses married and Florence, furiously protesting, could do nothing to prevent the nonsense!

Strangely, perhaps, Miss Nightingale was never an advocate of feminism. Though herself an outstanding example of a woman who had contended against prodigious odds and carved out a career in fields always before barred to her sex, she had no wish to vote. The devious ways of politics all were known to her; the methods and policies of government were like an open book. Yet she did not favor the participation of women in either politics or government. In a day when the woman suffrage sentiment was born, and struggled into the ascendancy, she was unresponsive. Several of her women friends were ardent champions of the feminist cause—she would not embrace it. Indeed, she seldom mentioned it, but went on working for the uplifting and salvation of the human race as a whole, not discriminating between the sexes. Probably she had never thought of herself as downtrodden or victimized by men (nor had she been!) and in her various campaigns she had labored beside men, trusting them and conscious of her equality with the best of them.

If this was an old-fashioned attitude, so also was her antagonism for the theory of microbes, developed through the scientific research of Pasteur and Lister. Bacteriology was a study she would never undertake, the idea that disease was spread by germs seemed absurd to her. She had not met with microbes in the Crimea—

at least, she thought she hadn't. No, she had met only with dirt, lack of proper food, ventilation and sanitary facilities; from them, not from germs, sickness and misery had resulted. These things she had seen and could therefore believe. But had she ever seen a microbe? Certainly not! She would not then acknowledge the existence of microbes. Dr. Sutherland infuriated her by his interest, his belief, in them.

During the years she was increasingly dependent upon Dr. Sutherland's help and companionship, and often very impatient with him. She consulted him about everything, and begrudged those hours which he spent away from South Street. He had a house at Norwood and a little garden in which he liked to relax. Florence disapproved of both house and garden, and if he said he could not immediately do whatever she asked of him, she flung reproaches at him. Sometimes Dr. Sutherland rebelled at this tyranny; but usually he did as he was told. His good humor was such that he forgave Miss Nightingale's scoldings. "Thanks for your parting kick," he once wrote, "which is always pleasant to receive by them as likes it." And he retorted with teasing. When Florence asked him to fill in her census form and define her occupation, he wrote "None!"

As one commentator has said, Dr. Sutherland's wife, who also was devoted to Miss Nightingale, must often have welcomed home a very tired and exasperated man.

21

TRIALS AND TRIUMPHS

To FLORENCE NIGHTINGALE must be given much of the world's gratitude for the International Red Cross Society. This most wonderful of all humanitarian organizations was founded by the Swiss philanthropist, Henri Dunant, as an aftermath of the battle of Solferino.

Speaking in London in 1872, Monsieur Dunant said: "What inspired me to go to Italy during the war of 1859 was the work of Miss Florence Nightingale in the Crimea."

Appealed to for encouragement and help in the framing of the earliest Red Cross Convention, Florence had joined the movement immediately; the British delegates setting out in 1864 for the International Congress were armed with her written instructions which were meticulously followed in every detail. With the outbreak of the Franco-Prussian War in 1870, more calls reached Florence in her South Street seclusion.

Though from the first a party to the Geneva Convention, the British government had done nothing toward the actual formation of a Red Cross Society, but now this step must be taken. What was more natural than to look to Miss Nightingale for leadership? The temporary committee appointed in 1870 conferred with Florence; and largely through her whole-hearted co-operation, the British Red Cross Aid Society soon emerged as a reality.

Miss Nightingale said that had she not been confined to a sick bed, she would have volunteered for service on the battle front. As it was, she could work only as her physical impairments permitted—but she would do her utmost! Her letters read at public meetings brought forth rounds of deafening applause and incited a general enthusiasm for the infant organization.

Throughout the Franco-Prussian War, Florence was closely involved with the work of the Red Cross, both in England and abroad. Relatives and friends of hers were sent to inspect the hospitals of France and Germany, and their reports returned to her; Dr. Sutherland attended to much of the Society's correspondence; and Florence herself was diligent in the collection of money and gifts for war sufferers.

Of course, she was deluged with inquiries of all sorts. The French asked her for plans for field hospitals; the Crown Princess of Prussia begged for advice and assistance. Later the Crown Princess came in person to South Street—a visit which resulted in the introduction of Nightingale nurses into Prussian hospitals and a great improvement in German nursing methods.

Florence's sympathies were rather with the French in this conflict; but she was conscientiously impartial and strove for the alleviation of distress in both countries.

Now that she was "out of office," she wrote extensively on religious subjects, picking up again the *Suggestions for Thought,* that book begun so long ago, when it had seemed she was forever imprisoned in the Embley drawing-room, and almost forgotten in the crowded after-years. Now she wished again to analyze her own religion. She was a churchwoman, but had never gone much to church—as superintendent for the Harley Street "gentle-women's" home, she used to hide on Sunday mornings so that the inmates would not be shocked to discover she was not a churchgoer. Her convictions were unorthodox, she knew, but very sincere and firm; she felt that she must crystallize and put neatly on paper her special creed, her confidence in God's infinite goodness.

In this she was urged on by Benjamin Jowett, the English scholar and theologian, master of Balliol College, Oxford, who had become perhaps her most intimate friend. Indeed, Dr. Jowett's cordiality compensated, to a degree, for the loss of Sidney Herbert, though this was an association of a different kind. Mr. Herbert had been Florence's partisan and collaborator; the master of Balliol sustained her with spiritual solace.

Yet even with Dr. Jowett's friendship to lean upon, and the series of voluminous letters they exchanged, and the expansion and clarifying of her *Suggestions for Thought,* she had many hours of utter dejection, when she was oppressed with the feeling of failure, futility. She was middle-aged, lonely; the isolation she had fostered and still clung to, did not bring happiness. Except when immersed in work, she had the nagging sensation of emptiness.

Insomnia troubled her; and at night, lying sleepless, she would reach for the pencil and notebook always on her bedside table and write memoranda of her reflections. Melancholy jottings they were, filled with doubt and self-reproach: "Oh, my Creator, Thou knowest that through all these 20 horrible years I have been supported by the belief that I was working with Thee Who wert bringing every one of us, even our poor nurses, to perfection."—"Oh, Lord my God, patience is very necessary for me, for I perceive that many things in this life do fall out as we would not."—"O Lord, even now I am trying to snatch the management of Thy world out of Thy hands." —"Too little have I looked for something higher and better than my own work."

In 1874 Florence's father died suddenly; and in the midst of mourning for him, she had to pause and see to legal and business affairs. Mr. Nightingale's sister, Aunt Mai Smith, was heir to his land and his two country houses, while his daughters, Parthe and Florence, inherited other properties. This meant that Mrs. Nightingale must be provided for. Mamma was eighty-six now, and Florence must be in part responsible for her. It was arranged that she should live in London with a nephew, but should have annual autumn sojourns at Lea Hurst.

Florence disliked the unavoidable interruptions of all such decisions. "Oh, God," she exclaimed, "let me not sink in these perplexities, but give me a great cause to do and die for! I am so disturbed by my family that I can't do my work."

But she and Mamma were now quite reconciled and on more affectionate terms than ever before. Mrs. Nightingale had ceased to be critical of this "swan" she had hatched. "You would have done nothing in life, Flo," she once said, "if you had not resisted me."

Florence was able to see her mother rather often in London and she visited her at Lea Hurst on several occasions. Once she rented a villa in Norwood and tried the experiment of their living together—which lasted for a period of a few weeks. The villa was painted red and was hideous; "like a monster lobster," Florence said, and she soon left it.

"This is the only time for 22 years," she wrote, "that

my work has not been the first cause for where I should live and how I should live. It is the caricature of a life!"

Mrs. Nightingale ended her days at Lea Hurst, a very, very old lady, whose mind had clouded. "Where is Florence?" she would ask. "Is she still in her hospital? I suppose she will never marry now."

As the years passed, Florence's health seemed to mend. The nervous malady disappeared; she was almost entirely well. After her mother's death, she never went back to Lea Hurst; but she saw something of Parthe, who, with her husband, had a house in South Street only a stone's throw distant from Florence's house. Sir Harry Verney's beautiful country place was Claydon, in Buckinghamshire; and infrequently Florence stayed there with her sister.

Florence had grown to be very fond of Sir Harry and had made friends with his children. Sometimes she drove in Sir Harry's carriage or walked in the park with him. In 1882 her health was so nearly normal that she accompanied Sir Harry to the opening of the new Law Courts —where she was recognized by Queen Victoria. "Look!" said the Queen, "Isn't that Miss Nightingale? It is, indeed!"

That same year she paid her first and only visit to St. Thomas' and with her own eyes saw the quarters of her nurses' training school. Again squired by Sir Harry, she witnessed the arrival of the Grenadier Guards at the railway station, fresh from their Egyptian campaign; and at Mr. Gladstone's invitation, she watched a military parade and review of the troops.

Her work in this period consisted of further reforms for India and a more comprehensive study of nursing

problems; and she accomplished much of value, fear-
lessly forging ahead into new and untried paths of progress. It was only habit, perhaps, which kept her shut

She witnessed the arrival of the Grenadier Guards

away most of the time in her bright, airy upper room, the
world shut out; she had come to prefer this sheltered
solitary existence, finding in it peace, order, and a retreat
from the acclaim which would surely have been heaped

upon her, had she opened her doors to the normal activities of life.

In 1891, Dr. Sutherland died, and then except for servants, she was quite alone at No. 10 South Street. But Dr. Jowett, her nurses and privileged friends continued to call. And she was always busy.

Her interest in the British army never abated. Any reference to the splendid character of England's fighting man would bring a sparkle to her glance, a smile to her lips.

"The soldier," she would remark, "is a very expensive article!" But how admirable he was, how deserving of all that was done for him!

On Balaclava Day, October 25, 1897, she wrote greetings to the Crimean veterans, addressing them as "My dear old Comrades." During the Boer War, she helped again with the nursing program.

22

FAREWELLS

SHE WAS SOFTER with the years, more amiable, her fiery mood mellowing.

She was softer with the years

Among the nurses at St. Thomas' were a favored few, young enough to be her granddaughters, with whom she was tender, endearing, nicknaming them as "The Pearl," or "The Goddess." She was thoughtful of all the young cousins in the family, and of Arthur Clough's children; she sent them presents and notes; she was "Ever your loving Aunt Florence." Advancing age made it necessary that she have a nurse to care for her, and she did not object. But at night, after the nurse had tucked her into bed, Florence would clamber out, patter into the next room and tuck in the nurse.

By her express wish she now lived very quietly, removed from stress and turmoil and well content to be, asking nothing but her precious solitude—and rest at last.

She refused to have her photograph taken and when she was besought to allow a statue of herself to be shown at Queen Victoria's Diamond Jubilee celebration in 1897, she replied, with a flash of her former temper, but smiling, "I won't be made a sign at an exhibition!"

Finally she yielded, and the statue was displayed.

"I hope it gets smashed!" said Florence.

The statue did not get smashed. Instead, it was decked each day with wreaths of flowers by people who delighted in the gesture of homage.

For though she was so old now, and the past slipping away into dimness, the century turning, Queen Victoria dead and Edward VII on the throne—though Florence Nightingale had renounced the world and its activities, she was still more than a memory to a nation which had adored her. She was still the idol she had always been. In December, 1908, England conferred upon her the Order of Merit, the greatest honor within the power of the realm to bestow, and the first time it had ever been offered a woman.

Sir Douglas Dawson, King Edward's emissary, brought the Order of Merit to her South Street chamber. There was no ceremony. Florence was eighty-eight, feeble; for months she had been rather vague about her surroundings, many things. Perhaps she didn't quite know who the gentleman was or why he had come. But she was polite, seemed to be appreciative.

"Too kind," she murmured. "Too kind."

She died August 13, 1910, between night and morning, falling asleep as usual and never waking. The government said she must be buried in Westminster Abbey —but the surviving relatives declined. Florence wouldn't have liked such pomp and circumstance; and, anyway, she had left directions about her funeral. It must be as simple as possible, she had said.

They buried her, then, at East Wellow, beside her father and mother, in the churchyard near Embley. Six stalwart army sergeants bore the flag-draped coffin along the country road, where the neighbors had gathered in a silent throng.

At the grave a hymn was sung, just one, but militant and challenging it was, appropriate to the day, the hour —to Florence Nightingale:

> "The son of God goes forth to war,
>   His blood-red banner streams afar . . .
> Who follows in His train?"